Music Literacy Workbook

Volume 1

by
Rebecca Berkley and Gavin Richards

R·

Rhinegold Publishing Ltd

241 Shaftesbury Avenue
London WC2H 8TF
Telephone: 020 7333 1720

Rhinegold Music Study Guides

(series editor: Paul Terry)

Students' Guides to GCSE, AS and A2 Music for the AQA, Edexcel and OCR Specifications

Listening Tests for GCSE, AS and A2 Music for the AQA, Edexcel and OCR Specifications

A Student's Guide to GCSE Music for the WJEC Music Specifications

A Student's Guide to Music Technology for the AS and A2 Specification

Listening Tests for the Edexcel AS and A2 Music Technology Specifications

Key Stage 3 Listening Tests: Book 1

Key Stage 3 Elements

Lifelines Revision Guides to GCSE, AS and A2 Music for the AQA and Edexcel Specifications

Lifelines Revision Guides to AS and A2 Music Technology for the Edexcel Specifications

A Student's Guide to Harmony and Counterpoint for AS and A2 Music

Also available from Rhinegold Publishing

Romanticism in Focus

Baroque Music in Focus

Madonna: *The Immaculate Collection* in Focus

The Who: *Who's Next* in Focus

Danny Elfman: *Batman* in Focus

John Barry: *Goldfinger* in Focus

Rhinegold Publishing also publishes Classical Music, Classroom Music, Early Music Today, Music Teacher, Opera Now, Piano, The Singer, Teaching Drama, British and International Music Yearbook, British Performing Arts Yearbook, Rhinegold Guide to Music Education, Rhinegold Dictionary of Music in Sound.

Other Rhinegold Study Guides

Rhinegold publishes resources for candidates studying Classical Civilisation, Drama and Theatre Studies, Performance Studies, and Religious Studies.

First published 2007 in Great Britain by
Rhinegold Publishing Ltd
241 Shaftesbury Avenue
London WC2H 8TF
Telephone: 020 7333 1720
Fax: 020 7333 1765
www.rhinegold.co.uk
© Rhinegold Publishing Ltd 2007

Rhinegold Publishing Ltd has used its best efforts in preparing this workbook. It does not assume, and hereby disclaims, any liability to any party for loss or damage caused by errors or omissions in the guide whether such errors or omissions result from negligence, accident or other cause.

Music Literacy Workbook: Volume 1

British Library Cataloguing in Publication Data.

A catalogue record for this book is available from the British Library.

ISBN: 978-1-906178-00-0

Printed in Great Britain by Thanet Press

Contents

Authors

Rebecca Berkley

Rebecca is a freelance writer and musician, and is a music education consultant. She has taught percussion to students of all ages, both as a private teacher and as a workshop leader, and published percussion music. She is also a choral conductor, running several choirs and directing music festivals with her husband. After starting her career as a music teacher in secondary schools, she became a lecturer in music education at the University of Southampton and the Institute of Education, University of London. Her PhD thesis focused on how GCSE students learn to compose, and how best to teach them. She is the co-author of Rhinegold Publishing's *Listening Tests* for *Students: Edexcel GCSE Music Specification* (Book 3) and contributes as a freelance writer to Rhinegold Publishing's *Classroom Music.*

Gavin Richards

Richard has been director of music at the Perse School in Cambridge since 2002. He has a music honours degree from Cambridge University and studied piano as a part-time student at the Royal Academy of Music. He has taught piano to students of all ages and has performed widely as a concerto and recital soloist – including a performance of Rachmaninov's Piano Concerto No 2 at the Symphony Hall in Birmingham. He created the MusicLand website, which has become one of the leading online communities for music education in the UK, and he too contributes as a freelance writer to Rhinegold Publishing's *Classroom Music.*

Editors

Lucien Jenkins, Chris Elcombe, Rose Vickridge, Sarah Smith, Zöe Franklin and Elisabeth Boulton.

Acknowledgements

The publishers and authors are grateful for the following publishers for permission to use excerpts from their publications:

Massachusetts. Words and Music by Barry Gibb, Maurice Gibb and Robin Gibb. © Copyright 1967 Gibb Brothers Music (66.67%), used by permission of Music Sales Limited. All Rights Reserved. International Copyright Secured. © 1967 BMG Music Publishing International and Crompton Songs; Warner/Chappell Music Ltd (33.33%). Reproduced by permission of Faber Music Ltd. All Rights Reserved.

Livin' On A Prayer: Words and Music by Richie Sambora, Desmond Child and Jon Bon Jovi. © Copyright 1986 EMI April Music Incorporated, Bon Jovi Publishing, Desmobile Music Company Incorporated, PolyGram International Music Publishing Incorporated, USA; Universal Music Publishing Limited (33.33%), Sony/ATV Music Publishing (UK) Limited (33.33%). Used by permission of Music Sales Limited. All Rights Reserved. International Copyright Secured. © 1985 Bon Jovi Publishing, Polygram International Publishing, Desmobile Inc, Aggressive Music and Sony-ATV Tume LLC; EMI Music Publishing Ltd (33.33%). Reproduced by permission of International Music Publications Ltd (a trading name of Faber Music Ltd). All Rights Reserved.

Yesterday. Words and Music by John Lennon and Paul McCartney. © Copyright 1965 Northern Songs. Used by permission of Music Sales Limited. All Rights Reserved. International Copyright Secured.

Kumbaya. Traditional. © Copyright 2005 Dorsey Brothers Music Limited. Used by permission of Music Sales Limited. All Rights Reserved. International Copyright Secured.

Catch A Falling Star. Words and Music by Paul J. Vance and Lee Pockriss. © Copyright 1957 (renewed 1985) Paul J. Vance Publishing Company and Emily Music Corporation, USA; Campbell Connelly & Company Limited. Used by permission of Music Sales Limited. All Rights Reserved. International Copyright Secured.

The Twelve Days Of Christmas. Traditional. © Copyright 2005 Dorsey Brothers Music Limited. Used by permission of Music Sales Limited. All Rights Reserved. International Copyright Secured.

Star Wars (Main Theme). Music by John Williams. © 1977 Bantha Music;Warner/Chappell North America Ltd. Reproduced by permission of Faber Music Ltd. All Rights Reserved.

Happy Birthday To You. Words and Music by Patty S. Hill and Mildred Hill. © 1935 (renewed 1962) Summy Birchard Inc and Keith Prowse Music Publishing Co Ltd; EMI Music Publishing Ltd. Reproduced by permission of International Music Publications Ltd (a trading name of Faber Music Ltd). All Rights Reserved.

Over the Rainbow. Words and Music by E Y Harburg and Harold Arlen. © 1938 EMI Catalogue Partnership and EMI Feist Catalog Inc, USA; EMI United Partnership Ltd (publishing) and Alfred Publishing Co, USA (print). Administered in Europe by Faber Music Ltd. All Rights Reserved.

Dance by Kabalevsky. © Copyright 1938 by Boosey & Hawkes Music Publishers Ltd for the United Kingdom and the republic of Ireland. Reproduced by kind permission of Boosey & Hawkes.

Preface

Reading which notion?

This book offers a new approach to mastering music theory and notation. It will help you learn how to read and understand a range of aspects of music literacy, and will show you how they relate to music from the middle ages to the present day – whether it is classical, rock and pop, jazz, blues or folk music.

You may have some experience of notation from the music that you play and sing, or you may be starting on it from scratch. Either way, there is useful and interesting information about reading and writing music in this book which will help you become more confident in both skills, and introduce you to new types of musical scores which will help you in your performing, composing and listening.

What is a score?

A score is a written record of music. It contains the written information the performers need in order to create the music. Some of the music is put on paper as musical symbols and some is written as text. The umbrella term for this collection of symbols and text is music notation

The symbols and text that we see in a score include information about pitch, rhythm, style, structure and (where necessary) lyrics: we shall be looking at these one by one.

Why is it useful to read and write music?

Music notation is a common language among musicians who play western classical music, but it's also used by plenty of people in the worlds of rock, pop and jazz. Performers can play music created by composers by reading the music they have written. Composers use notation to work out their musical ideas. It is a quick and easy way of recording ideas, and getting the music played again by other musicians. It does not matter whether musicians write their ideas down with pencil and paper or use music technology. The important thing is to be able to understand this musical language, and use it wherever possible.

Music notation for performers is like a recipe for a chef. A recipe lists the ingredients and presents a method for making the food, and then it is up to the chef to bring the food to life. In the same way, music notation gives the performer a code to follow when they are making a performance. Just as recipes can be written for any type of food, so performers can use scores to perform any type of music. The written instructions musicians work from can be exact, where every single musical idea is notated, or it can be an outline of the key ideas in the piece, giving them the chance to improvise or compose some more music for themselves as they perform.

For the composer, music notation is both a record of their musical ideas and a helpful tool for planning new pieces. Once they have worked out their initial ideas, the composer can write them down and keep an accurate record of their work, rather than having to try to remember it. Writing down ideas helps the composer think about the detail of the music they are creating, and can help the composer to work out precisely what they want in their composition. Using notation also means that a composer can create music for other musicians to play live, and to compose for instruments that they don't play themselves.

For someone doing listening and appraising work, notation is a map of the music. It contains all the information about what is going on in the piece, and gives the listener a visual record of what they are listening to. Following the score while listening – score reading – helps the listener to find significant elements and ideas in the music. Score reading helps the listener to work out how the composer has created the mood and style by identifying what special techniques and devices they have used to create these effects.

Staff notation

Staff notation, the system taught in this book, has various claims to your attention, but here are four:

1. Unlike lots of systems, it's the same for all instruments

2. It's a bit like reading words in a European language: we read it from left to right

3. How it's written looks a bit like what it does: when the notes come one after the other, they are played one after the other; when they are lined up vertically on top of one another, then they are played together

4. It's international: you can pull out a sheet of staff notation anywhere in the world where western classical music is taught, and find people who can read it.

It isn't a perfect system, and there are some things it's better at and others it's worse at. But being literate in it is definitely a useful skill to acquire, regardless of where you plan on being, and what kind of music you want to play, compose or study.

Using this book

Each chapter explains an aspect of music notation stage by stage, offering exercises to practise each point as it is introduced. To put theory into practice, it is good to play or sing through music examples to help build up your sight-reading skills. A few exercises are self-sufficient and everything you need to complete them is in front of you on the page. Most of them require you to write in answers, and then check against the answers provided at the back of the book. There are also revision exercises at various points in the book to help consolidate your knowledge as you progress. Never check the answers while still working on an exercise. To make things clear, we've made notation where you're expected to write larger than other music examples. The same is true of tables where you are supposed to write the answers and fill in blanks.

We encourage you to notate music as much as possible. Where we offer the opportunity to write notes on a stave, we make it a little bit larger than those that are purely for reading to make it easier for you to be neat and accurate. And what's a stave? Well, that's all part of what this book sets out to explain.

1. Starting out with rhythm and pitch

Rhythm

When we write a note we give two main pieces of information about it:

➢ How long it lasts for (its length)

➢ How high or low it is (its pitch).

We will be looking at pitch later in this chapter. First, we will learn about the lengths of notes.

Note lengths

As a very general rule the more ink you have on a note the shorter its length.
The following table illustrates this point:

What the note looks like	o	𝅗𝅥	♩	♪	♬
Number of units	4	2	1	½	¼
Name of note	Semibreve	Minim	Crotchet	Quaver	Semiquaver
American name	Whole note	Half note	Quarter note	Eighth note	Sixteenth note

It is helpful to think of a crotchet as lasting for one 'unit'. The lengths of other notes are all relative to this. For example, a minim (two units) is twice as long as a crotchet and a crotchet is twice as long as a quaver (half a unit).

Exercise 1

Add up the number of units in the following rhythmic patterns.
The first one has been done for you.

	Rhythmic pattern	Number of units
1.	o 𝅗𝅥 𝅗𝅥	8
2.	𝅗𝅥 𝅗𝅥 ♩ ♩ 𝅗𝅥 ♩ ♩	
3.	o 𝅗𝅥 ♩ ♩ ♩ ♩ ♩ ♩	
4.	♩ 𝅗𝅥 𝅗𝅥. o ♩ ♩ ♩ ♩ ♪ ♪ ♩	
5.	♩ ♪ ♪ ♪ ♪ ♪ ♪ ♩ 𝅗𝅥	
6.	♩ ♩ ♩ ♩ ♬ ♬ ♬ ♩	

Exercise 2

Now, add an extra note to the following rhythms so that they add up to the number of units stated. The first one has been done for you.

	Starting rhythm	Number of units	Extra note needed
1.	𝅝	6	𝅗𝅥
2.	𝅗𝅥 𝅗𝅥 𝅗𝅥 ♩ ♩	9	
3.	𝅝 𝅝 𝅗𝅥 ♩ ♩ ♩ ♩	14	
4.	𝅗𝅥 ♩ ♩ ♩ ♩ ♩ ♪ ♪ ♪	9	
5.	♪ ♪ ♪ ♪ ♪ 𝅗𝅥 𝅝	11	

Now that you are familiar with the different note values, it is time to put them into a musical context.

First, we need to know how long each unit is. To work this out, we need to think about the beat of the music.

The beat of a piece of music is what you tap your foot to. We can also call this the pulse. Listen to any piece of pop music and you will probably find your foot tapping along to the beat.

The beat can be fast (as in many club or dance tracks), medium (as in many disco songs) or slow (as in many ballads).

Have a look at these rhythms which use some of the notes we have looked at so far.

Remember: the beat (or pulse) must be regular. Count '1' for crotchets and '1, 2' for minims.

Have a go at clapping these rhythms or playing them on a classroom percussion instrument. How many beats are there in each example? Try playing the rhythms with a fast beat, a medium beat or a slow beat.

When you are confident with clapping these short rhythms accurately, try clapping or tapping the following rhythm which is a little longer:

Did you find this rhythm more difficult? Did you lose your place when clapping it? It would have been even harder to follow if it had contained lots of different note lengths. It is difficult to follow an unbroken series of notes. This is why we divide our music into shorter chunks. These chunks are called bars and they are usually of equal length.

Let's organise the above rhythm into bars of four beats:

Each bar is separated by a **bar line**. The bar line does not affect your performance of a piece – you musn't hesitate at **bar lines**! It is there to help you follow the music more easily, and stop you getting lost.

Beats in a bar and time signature

The **time signature** tells us how many beats there are in each bar.

2
2

4
4

The lower number is often 2 or 4. (Sometimes it is 8, but we will talk about this more in Chapter 3.)

Remember, the beat is what you tap your foot to!

Now look at the rhythm above with four bars of four beats. It has a time signature of **4/4** – check that the notes in every bar add up correctly!

Time signatures of **2/4**, **3/4** and **4/4** are very common. They are known as simple time signatures (not because they are easy – we will find out more about this later.)

To sum up:

2/4 – Two crotchet beats in every bar (good for marching!)

3/4 – Three crotchet beats in every bar (good for waltzing!)

4/4 – Four crotchet beats in every bar (good for disco dancing!)

You may also see this symbol as a time signature: **C**

You can think of the **C** symbol standing for 'common time'. It was used in early music and is another way of writing **4/4** – so music with this symbol always has four crotchet beats in a bar.

When we write a rhythm we can use a percussion stave. All the notes sit on a single line, like this:

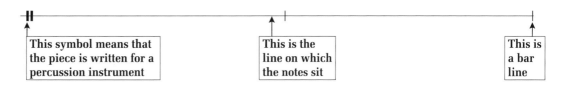

This symbol means that the piece is written for a percussion instrument

This is the line on which the notes sit

This is a bar line

Exercise 3

For each of the following four rhythms add an appropriate time signature at the start, either **2/4**, **3/4** or **4/4**.

These notes are two quavers joined (or beamed) together – we will look at how to do this later on.

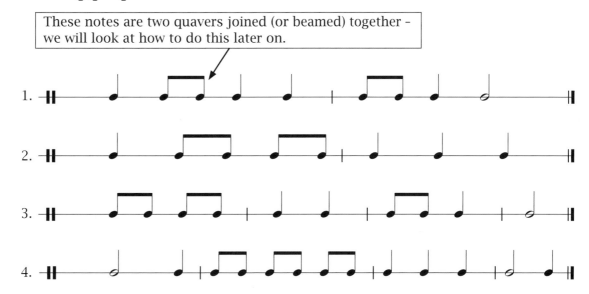

Exercise 4

In the following rhythms the time signature is given but the bar lines are missing. Write the bar lines in the correct place.

Exercise 5

Now have a go at clapping the following rhythms or playing them on a percussion instrument. For each rhythm, try it at a fast, medium and slow beat.

Listening to music with different time signatures

The following pieces of music are good examples of $\frac{2}{4}$, $\frac{3}{4}$ and $\frac{4}{4}$ time. Try to listen to a selection of them (they can easily be bought on CD or downloaded using iTunes or a similar purchasing programme). This will help you gain a feel for the different time signatures. Decide if each piece of music has a fast, medium or slow beat.

Time signature	Pieces in which it might be found	Examples
$\frac{2}{4}$	Polkas, Marches	➢ *Unter Donner und Blitz* ('Thunder and Lightning') Polka by Johann Strauss ➢ *The Liberty Bell March* by Sousa ➢ March from *Superman* by Williams ➢ *Crown Imperial March* by Walton
$\frac{3}{4}$	Waltzes, Minuets, Scherzos	➢ Minuet from *Anna Magdalena Notebook* by J S Bach ➢ Scherzo No 2 in B♭ minor by Chopin ➢ *The Waltz* by Dave Brubeck
$\frac{4}{4}$	Widely used in classical and popular music, e.g. rock and disco	➢ 'Spring' from *The Four Seasons* by Vivaldi ➢ Piano Concerto No 2, 3rd movt, by Rachmaninov ➢ *Natural Blues* by Moby ➢ *September* by Earth, Wind and Fire

Rests

A **rest** is a period of silence in music. For every note length we have looked at so far there is an equivalent rest. Like the notes, the *length* of the silence is shown by using different symbols. Rests help bring a piece of music to life and are particularly useful for woodwind, brass and vocal music (to help with the breathing!).

Here are the note lengths again, with their equivalent rests:

What the note looks like	𝅝	𝅗𝅥	♩	♪	𝅘𝅥𝅯
What the rest looks like	𝄻	𝄼	𝄽	𝄾	𝄿
Number of units	4	2	1	½	¼
Name of note	Semibreve	Minim	Crotchet	Quaver	Semiquaver

When you are composing a piece of music you can substitute a note for its equivalent rest, but make sure that the bar still adds up correctly. Let's practise working with a mixture of notes and rests.

Exercise 6

Add up the total number of beats in the following rhythmic patterns, which are made up of a mixture of notes and rests. The first one has been done for you.

	Rhythmic Pattern	Number of Beats
1.	𝅝 𝄼 𝄽 𝅗𝅥	12
2.	𝄽 𝅗𝅥 𝄾 𝅘𝅥 𝄾 𝅘𝅥 𝄾 𝅘𝅥 𝄽	
3.	𝄽 𝅘𝅥 𝄿 𝅘𝅥 𝄿 𝅘𝅥 𝄾	
4.	𝄾 𝅗𝅥 𝄾 𝅘𝅥𝅮𝅘𝅥𝅮𝅘𝅥𝅮 𝄿 𝅘𝅥𝅮 𝄿 𝅘𝅥𝅮 𝄿	
5.	𝅘𝅥𝅮𝅘𝅥𝅮𝅘𝅥 𝅘𝅥𝅘𝅥 𝄿 𝅘𝅥𝅮 𝄿 𝅘𝅥𝅝	
6.	𝅘𝅥𝅮𝅘𝅥𝅮𝅘𝅥𝅮𝅘𝅥𝅮𝅘𝅥 𝅘𝅥 𝄾 𝅝 𝄿 𝅘𝅥𝅮 𝄿 𝅘𝅥𝅮	

Exercise 7

Here are four rhythms consisting of notes and rests. Have a look at the time signatures and add the bar lines in the correct place.

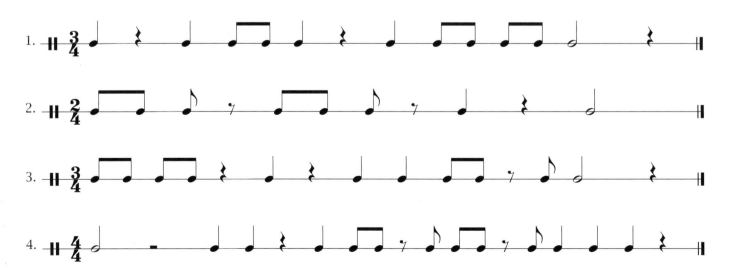

Here are some points to bear in mind when you're working with rests:

➢ Semibreve and minim rests can be confusing as they look similar. When we come to five-line staves in the next section, remember that the minim rest sits on the middle line of the stave, while the semibreve rests hangs underneath the fourth line up. There's an example on page 22.

➢ Although a semibreve rest is designed to show four beats it can also be used as a whole-bar rest, regardless of the length of the bar. Note also that a semibreve rest is written in the middle of the bar, rather than at the beginning of it.

➢ The crotchet rest is probably the most tricky to draw and worth some practice!

Beaming notes

We have seen above that notes with smaller values, such as quavers, can be **beamed** together. This is so that they can be grouped together into beats. Use the following guidelines when deciding whether to beam notes together or not.

DO:

➢ Beam notes together that belong to the same beat (a quaver and two semiquavers, or four semiquavers can be joined together)

➢ Beam up to four notes together at once.

So, this: is better written as this:

DON'T:

➢ Beam across the middle of a bar in $\frac{4}{4}$ time

➢ Beam together odd numbers of quavers when the time signature is $\frac{2}{4}$, $\frac{3}{4}$ or $\frac{4}{4}$.

So, this: is better written as this:

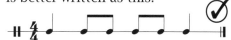

Exercise 8

Rewrite the following two rhythms with the quaver notes beamed together correctly:

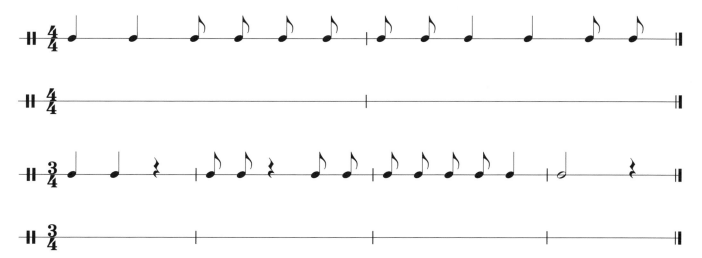

Now that we understand the building blocks of rhythm, it is time to look at the pitch of the notes.

Pitch

Pitch means how high or low the note is. We use pitch notation for vocal music and for any instrument that can play a tune.

If you look at the first part of *Twinkle Twinkle, Little Star* below, you will see that the notes are written on five lines - this is called a stave. The notes are drawn in different places on, or between, the lines of the stave. It is the round part of the note which tells us the pitch. The higher the pitch, the higher the note is drawn on the stave.

Trad: *Twinkle twinkle, Little Star*

Lower note   Higher note

Letter names

We also use letter names to indicate pitch in music (written down as capitals). We use the first seven letters of the alphabet:

A B C D E F G.

You can start anywhere in the pattern and repeat it continuously. So, if you start on E the pattern will be: E F G A B C D E, and so on. If you go backwards from E the pattern will be: E D C B A G F E, and so on.

Exercise 9

Write down the correct order of letter names starting on the specified notes, and either going up or down, as indicated. Put one letter in each box. The first one has been done for you.

1. | C *going up* | C | D | E | F | G | A | B | C |
|---|---|---|---|---|---|---|---|---|

2. | A *going down* | | | | | | | | |
|---|---|---|---|---|---|---|---|---|

3. | F *going up* | | | | | | | | |
|---|---|---|---|---|---|---|---|---|

4. | G *going up* | | | | | | | | |
|---|---|---|---|---|---|---|---|---|

5. | B *going down* | | | | | | | | |
|---|---|---|---|---|---|---|---|---|

Drawing notes on the stave

Let's have a look at the five lines of the stave again.

 These five lines are also sometimes called a **staff**, and this way of writing down music is called **staff notation**. We draw notes on the lines and spaces as on the left.

We draw a **clef** at the start of each stave. The two most commonly used clefs are:

the **treble clef**   and the **bass clef**

The clef tells you which letter name to give each note on the lines and spaces of the stave. These are the letter names we give the notes in the **treble clef**:

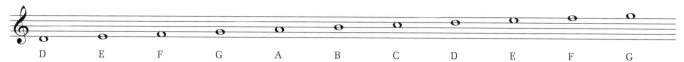

D E F G A B C D E F G

and these are the letter names we give the notes in the **bass clef**:

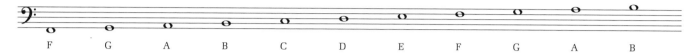

F G A B C D E F G A B

The treble clef is used for higher instruments, like violin, oboe, flute, alto sax, trumpet and xylophone, and for soprano, alto and treble voices. Here is the start of *Twinkle Twinkle, Little Star* written in the treble clef:

The bass clef is used for lower instruments, like bass guitar, cello, bassoon and trombone, and for bass voices. Here is the start of *Twinkle Twinkle, Little Star* written in the bass clef:

If you play the harp, or keyboard instruments like the piano or harpsichord, then your music is written on two staves and you read both at once. Remember that when things are lined up vertically in music you read and play the two staves together. The curly bracket at the beginning of the two staves tells the performer to read them together. Here is the start of *Twinkle Twinkle, Little Star* written out for the piano:

> The **stem** is the vertical line attached to the note head.

When drawing notes with **stems** in any clef, make sure that the notes that sit below the middle line of the stave are drawn with their stems pointing **upwards** and on the **right** hand side of the note, like this:

And notes with **stems** that sit above the middle line of the stave are drawn with their stems pointing **downwards** and on the **left** hand side of the note, like this:

The notes that sit on the middle line can be drawn with their stems pointing either way.

Exercise 10

Look at this list of instruments and voices, and decide which clef the performer would usually use. For some, the performer may use both clefs. The first one has been done for you.

Name of instrument or voice	Clef
Piano	Treble and bass together
Violin	
Soprano (voice)	
Descant recorder	
Timpani	
Oboe	
Tuba	
Bass (voice)	
Glockenspiel	
Flute	
Trumpet	

Drawing a treble clef

Have a go at drawing a treble clef on the blank stave below. Follow these simple steps (remember, your pen should never leave the paper):

1. Draw a dot on the second line up

2. Start a clockwise spiral that touches the line above and goes down again to the right of the dot, and then touches the line below the dot

3. Continue the line up to the left of the dot and up to make a loop just above the stave

4. Bring the line back down vertically, through the original dot, and finish with a curly tail.

Drawing a bass clef

Now try drawing a bass clef. Following these steps:

1. Draw a dot on the fourth line up

2. Begin a clockwise spiral that touches the line above, but carries on into the tail of the clef

3. Add two dots: drawn either side of the fourth line up.

It might help to think of the treble and bass clefs as fancily written versions of the letters **G** and **F** (which draw attention to the G and F lines of the stave).

Remembering the notes on the stave

A good way to remember the notes of the treble and bass clefs is to separate them into two groups: those drawn on the lines and those drawn on the spaces. Here are the notes of the treble clef:

E   G   B   D   F   F   A   C   E

And here are the notes of the bass clef:

G   B   D   F   A   A   C   E   G

You can make up words or sentences to remember the order of letters. In the treble clef, you could try:

Every **G**reen **B**us **D**rives **F**ast (for the lines)

F A C E (for the spaces)

And in the bass clef you could try:

Great **B**ig **D**ogs **F**rom **A**merica (for the lines)

All **C**ows **E**at **G**rass (for the spaces).

Why don't you make up some sentences of your own, to remember the order of letters.

Treble clef lines:

....

....

Treble clef spaces:

....

....

Bass clef lines:

....

....

Bass clef spaces:

....

....

Leger lines

If we need to go above or below the stave in a piece of music we use **leger lines**. These are additional small lines drawn in for each note. Here are some leger lines in the treble and bass clef:

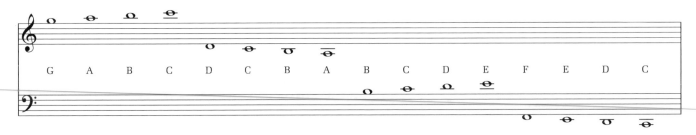

Only draw the leger lines you need. So, if you're drawing notes above the stave, only draw the **bottom** line of a note that's in a space. Similarly, notes in spaces **below** the stave need only the line **above** them. For instance, on the left are the notes G and D, with both the top and bottom lines drawn in. That's the wrong way to do it.

However, the example below it is how it should look in a piece of music.

As we said before, the pattern of letter names keeps on repeating, as you go up or down in pitch. You can use as many leger lines as you want, but normally you will only see one, two or three leger lines in music.

Here are all the notes of the treble and bass clef we have met so far:

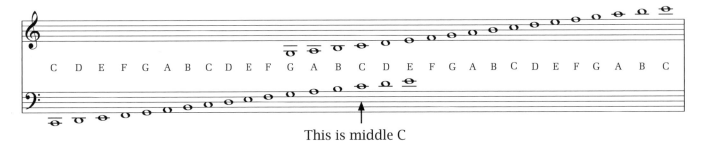

This is middle C

Here are the same notes on a keyboard:

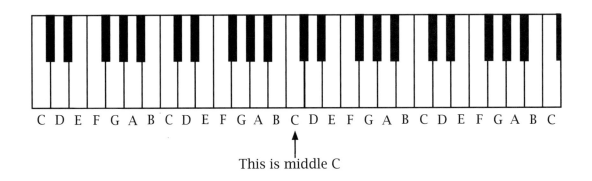

This is middle C

Exercise 11

Look at the melodies below and write in the letter name under each note (remember to use capital letters). Now have a go at playing them on an instrument.

Trad: *Twinkle Twinkle, Little Star*

J S Bach: Minuet

Kirkpatrick: *Away in a Manger*

Trad: *Over the Hills and Far Away*

<table>
<tr><td>

Keywords

Bass clef, clef, leger lines, letter names, lines and spaces, pitch, stave, treble clef.

</td></tr>
</table>

Revision exercise

Complete the following paragraph, using the keywords on the left.

We use _____ written as capital letters to indicate pitch in music. We draw notes on a set of five lines called a _____, and can place notes on the _____. At the start of each stave we draw a _____. For higher pitched music we use a _____ _____, and for lower pitched music we use a _____. _____. If we need to write notes that go above or below the stave, we use _____.

2. Moving on with rhythm and pitch

Adapting note lengths: dots, ties and triplets

So far we have looked at the basic building blocks of rhythm and pitch. Although *everything* we have covered so far is essential, it does not let us do everything we might want as composers. Suppose we wanted a note that lasted for one and a half units? Or three and a half units?

We will now look at a number of ways to adapt note lengths, including using dots, ties and triplets.

Adding a dot

> Be careful not to confuse this kind of dot, which is written after a note, with a staccato dot, which is written above or below a note. We shall be looking at staccato in Chapter 5.

A dot immediately to the right of the note affects its length. It increases the value of the note by **50 per cent** (i.e. half as much again).

This is how a dotted minim looks:

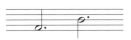

The dot goes to the right of the note. If the note is written on a line, then the dot goes just above the line, so it can be seen.

A **dotted minim** equals a minim (two units) plus a crotchet (one unit) – therefore it lasts for three units.

A **dotted crotchet** equals a crotchet (one unit) plus a quaver (half a unit) – therefore it lasts for one and a half units.

A **dotted quaver** equals a quaver (half a unit) plus a semiquaver (quarter of a unit) – therefore it lasts for three quarters of a unit. It is often followed by a semiquaver to make one unit in total.

Exercise 1

Add one dotted note to each of the following bars where there is an asterisk. Make sure each bar adds up to the correct number of units by looking carefully at the time signatures.

Be careful not to confuse this kind of curved line with phrase marks or slurs, which we shall come to in Chapter 5.

Tied notes

Ties are curved lines that join two or more notes of the same pitch together into one note of longer length. There are two situations when you would use ties:

1. The note value you want to create does not exist, for example a minim plus a quaver. This particular note value (two-and-a-half units) cannot be made by adding a dot.

2. You cannot fit the note you want into the remaining space of a bar, and you therefore need to join two notes together across a bar line.

You can only tie notes together. You cannot join rests with a tie.

Try clapping the following rhythm which uses some tied notes:

A = a minim tied to a quaver (this makes a note worth two-and-a-half units).
B = a crotchet tied to a quaver (the tie is needed to join two notes across the bar line).
C = a minim tied to a semibreve (this crosses a bar line and makes a note worth six units).

Exercise 2

Rewrite the following melodies into four bars of $\frac{4}{4}$ time on the blank staves below. You will need to make sure the bar lines fall in the right place. You may need to split some of the notes into two and tie them across the bar line.

Anacrusis

The above melodies are all extracts from a well known folk tune called *Londonderry Air*. The first half of this tune is shown on the next page. Try clapping it first and then have a go at performing it on a keyboard or other instrument. Do you notice anything odd about the way the units in the bars add up at the beginning and end?

Trad: *Londonderry Air*

The time signature is $\frac{4}{4}$ so we expect there to be four crotchets in a bar. However, the first bar has three crotchets and the last bar only has one. An incomplete bar at the start is known as an **anacrusis** (or **pick-up**). Sometimes an anacrusis may be only one beat in length, or even less. Usually the length of the final bar is reduced so that a complete bar's worth of notes is formed by adding together the anacrusis and the final bar. For instance, in the example above, the anacrusis is three beats long and the final bar is one beat long – together they add up to one full bar in $\frac{4}{4}$ time.

Here is another melody which uses a mixture of dotted notes, tied notes and rests. Try clapping it first and then, once you are happy with the rhythm, try playing the melody.

The Gibb Brothers (The BeeGees): *Massachusetts*

Triplets

Look at the melody below. What do you notice about the way the quavers have been written?

Williams: *Star Wars* - theme

The quavers have been grouped into units, each made up of three notes.

At first, it looks as though there are too many notes in each bar. We know that a crotchet beat can normally be divided into *two* quavers. Here the crotchet beats seem to be divided into *three* quavers.

These groupings are called **triplets**. When you see these it means you need to play **three quavers in the time of two**. They will therefore be a little faster than quavers.

To show a triplet, you need to write '3' by the beams, as in the example above.

Exercise 3

The bar lines are missing in the following rhythms. Add them in, remembering that each triplet of quavers counts as two quavers.

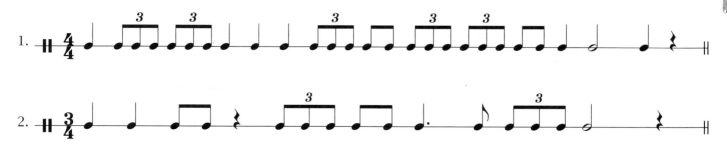

Now compose your own rhythm that uses a mixture of normal quaver (duplet) and triplet rhythms.

<table>
<tr><td>**Keywords**
Anacrusis, dotted notes, tied notes, triplets.</td><td>Now that we have looked at ways of adapting the rhythmic values, we will move on to look at ways of adapting the pitches.</td></tr>
</table>

Sharps, flats and naturals

If you look at a keyboard you will notice that so far all the notes we have discussed can be played on white keys. These are **natural** notes and, strictly speaking, each one should be called C natural (or C♮), D natural (or D♮), and so on. We don't normally bother doing this, and usually call them just by their letter names.

Here is the opening of Tallis' Canon with its letter names written in as naturals:

But we would normally write the letter names like this:

C C B C C D D E C F F E E D D C

Sharps, flats and naturals all alter the pitch of the note, and when you see them in the music you need to play or sing different notes. We use ♮ as a natural sign, ♯ as a sharp sign, and ♭ as a flat sign. So, for example, we would write: G♮ (G natural), G♯ (G sharp), and G♭ (G flat).

The closest gap between two notes on a keyboard is called a **semitone**. If you wanted to play G♯ on a keyboard, you would play the note which is a semitone above G (going up, to the right). If you wanted to play G♭, you would play the note which is a semitone below G (going down, to the left).

Here is a picture of the sharps, flats and naturals on the keyboard:

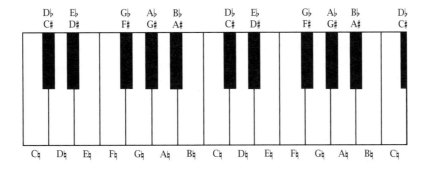

Notice how the pattern repeats along the keyboard.

Every letter has a natural, sharp and flat. So, there is G natural (G♮), G sharp (G♯), and G flat (G♭); A natural (A♮), A sharp (A♯), A flat (A♭); and so on.

You write the natural sign (♮), the sharp sign (♯) or the flat sign (♭) immediately before the note on the stave, and read the two symbols together. Here is the opening of Tallis' Canon using different notes:

F♮   F♯   E♮   F♮   F♮   G♮   G♮   A♮   F♮   B♭   B♭   A♮   A♮   G♮   G♮   F♮

Sharps, flats and naturals are drawn on the lines and spaces like notes. It is important to position any sharp, flat or natural on the same line or space as the note it relates to. Also, although we say 'B flat' we write ♭B on the stave (so the sharp, flat or natural is written *before* the note).

Enharmonic notes

Find F on a keyboard. Now find F♭ by playing the note which is a semitone *lower* than F. You will notice that F♭ is not a black key, but a white key, and the same key you press to play E.

Exercise 4

Now find E♯, B♯ and C♭ on a keyboard and complete this table:

F♭	is a semitone *lower* than F, and is the same white key as the note	E
E♯	is a semitone .... than E, and is the same white key as the note	
B♯	is a semitone .... than B, and is the same white key as the note	
C♭	is a semitone .... than C, and is the same white key as the note	

What happens when you play G♯ and then A♭ on a keyboard? Or C♯ and D♭? Or A♯ and B♭? As you will have noticed, you press the same key to play each of these pairs of notes. Notes which sound the same but are written differently, such as G♯ and A♭, or F♭ and E, are called **enharmonic notes**.

Key signatures and accidentals

If a piece of music uses the same set of sharps or flats consistently, then they can be drawn at the beginning of the stave as a **key signature**. Have a look at the whole of Tallis' Canon, shown below. There is a B♭ drawn at the start of every stave, which tells the performer that every B in the piece is played as a B♭. (We shall look at key signatures in more detail in Chapter 4.)

This is the key signature

F   F   E   F   F   G   G   A   F   B♭   B♭   A   A   G   G   F   C

B♭   G   A   A   G   G   F   C   D   E   F   A   G   G   F

Any extra sharps, flats or naturals that we write in the music are called **accidentals**.

Accidentals change the pitch of the notes they are written against, and last for the rest of the bar in which they occur, unless they are cancelled out by another accidental affecting the same note. Here is the beginning of Purcell's Rondo:

If you look at the opening of *I'm Forever Blowing Bubbles* below you will see a C♯ added as an accidental in bar 1. The next note is C♮ in bar 2. While the bar line cancels out the C♯, we can still add an extra natural sign to the following C♮, to remind us that the pitch of the note is different.

Kellette: *I'm Forever Blowing Bubbles*

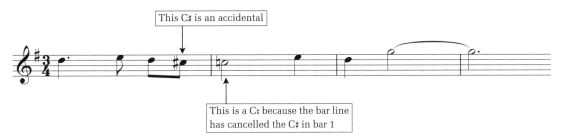

Exercise 5

Write in the names of the notes in the following melodies, including sharps and flats as necessary. Now have a go at playing the melodies.

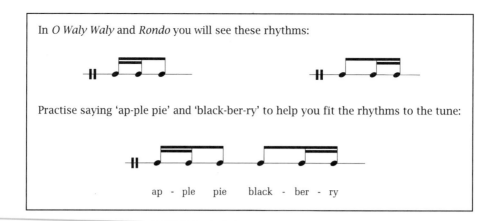

In *O Waly Waly* and *Rondo* you will see these rhythms:

Practise saying 'ap-ple pie' and 'black-ber-ry' to help you fit the rhythms to the tune:

ap - ple   pie   black - ber - ry

How to speed-read music

It can take a long time to work out the letter name of every note in a tune – and even longer to write them all in! We'll now look at some techniques to speed-read music.

Spot the repeated notes in a melody

When a tune has repeated notes in it, you only need to work out the first note and then repeat it, making sure you stick to the correct rhythm. Try playing *Catch a Falling Star*, below. The repeated notes have been marked for you.

Vance: *Catch a Falling Star*

Notice that in the above melody the note that is repeated changes in each bar. For instance, in bar 1 you play 'EEEEE', and in bar 2 you play 'GGGGG', and so on.

Spot notes that move in step

Notes move step-wise when the letter names follow the pattern 'A B C D E F G', either forwards or backwards, or when the notes are drawn 'line space, line space', on the stave, whether going up or down. This applies whether the notes are naturals, flats or sharps.

Try playing *Catch a Falling Star* again. The places where the melody moves step-wise have been marked below. When reading the step-wise patterns, work out the letter name of the first note in each group and then play up or down as the line of the music indicates. Watch out for the accidentals in the second and third line!

Spot repeated patterns in the melody

Most melodies include some repeated ideas or motifs. These might be repeated rhythms or repeated pitches. If you can identify these as you are playing the music, you don't need to work out the letter names the second or third time the motif is played. In *Catch a Falling Star* there are three main sections. The last section is an exact repeat of the first (labelled below as A – B – A).

Within each section there are some smaller ideas called 'motifs' that are also repeated. As you can see below, in Section A the opening motif is used several times:

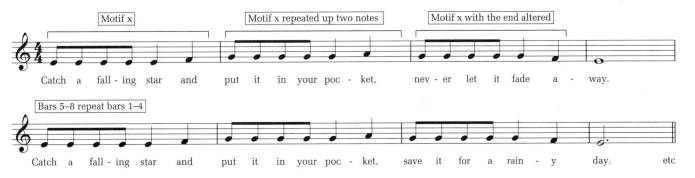

Exercise 6

Go back through the melodies in this chapter and mark in where they have:

➢ Repeated notes

➢ Step-wise movement

➢ Repeated motifs.

Try rubbing out as many letter names as you can and test yourself with your speed-reading.

Keywords
accidentals,
flats, key
signature,
naturals,
sharps.

Revision exercise

Match the keywords with the definitions. The first one has been done for you.

Accidentals	⟶	Sharps, flats or naturals which are written in the music, but are not in the key signature
Key signature		A sign which indicates that a note is a semitone lower than its normal unaltered pitch
Natural (♮)		A collection of sharps or flats written at the start of every stave
Sharp (♯)		A sign cancelling the effect of a previous sharp or flat written either as an accidental or in the key signature
Flat (♭)		A sign which indicates that a note is a semitone higher than its normal unaltered pitch.

3. Stepping out: more about rhythm

'How fast does it go?' is one of the first questions you ask when trying to play a new piece of music. In this chapter we're going to look in more detail at **tempo**.

Composers usually indicate the speed of their music by means of a **tempo marking**.

Tempo markings normally appear at the beginning of the piece, like the 'Allegro' marking in the following example:

J S Bach: Minuet

This is a tempo instruction. Allegro means 'quickly'.

You can introduce a change of tempo, by using a new marking at any later point in a piece.

You will find tempo markings given in either, or both, of the following ways:

➢ A word or a phrase

➢ A number (called a metronome marking - we will be looking at this in more detail later).

Tempo markings given in words

Tempo markings are often in Italian, though you may also see French and German instructions. Modern British composers often use English instructions in their pieces. You will still need to become familiar with the key Italian vocabulary, however, so that you can understand it when you see it in music you are performing, and you may even choose to use it in your own compositions.

Here are some common Italian terms you might see, together with their English translations:

Italian term	English translation
Adagio	Slow
Largo	Slow and stately
Andante	Walking pace
Moderato	Moderate speed
Allegro	Quick
Vivace	Lively
Presto	Very quick
Prestissimo	As fast as possible

You will notice that the differences in meaning between some of the tempo markings are very slight. Tempo markings are not an exact science but they give the musician a general idea of how fast or slow the tempo should be.

Try listening to the following pieces to get a feel for different tempos. Some pieces have a tempo marking in their title, which gives a good clue as to the speed. This list might also give you some ideas for some additional pieces you may like to listen to or play.

Largo	Largo from the *New World Symphony* by Dvořák
Adagio	*Adagio for Strings* by Barber
Andante	Andante from *Brandenburg Concerto* No 4 by J S Bach

Allegro	*Eine Kleine Nachtmusik*, 1st movement, by Mozart
	Waterloo by Abba
Presto	Mambo from *Symphonic Dances* by Bernstein
Prestissimo	The final bars of Symphony No 9 by Beethoven
	Feuillets d'Album for Piano, 3rd movement (Gigue), by Poulenc

Metronome markings

While Italian tempo markings are used to suggest a general sense of the speed, a metronome marking is a more exact way of defining the tempo.

A metronome is a device which produces any number of clicks per minute. They used to be mechanical and clockwork, but many are now electronic and digital. However, their function is still the same - they enable you to interpret a metronome marking, which may look something like this:

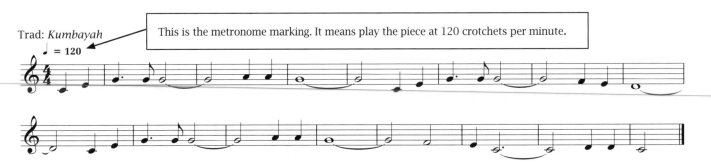

Trad: *Kumbayah*

♩ = 120

This is the metronome marking. It means play the piece at 120 crotchets per minute.

Remember...

that the **beat** or **pulse** is what you tap your foot to. The **tempo** is how fast you're tapping it!

The metronome is 'tapping your foot' for you - telling you when the beats are. By setting it to 120, you are telling it the tempo - how fast to tap the beats.

If you do not have a metronome, you can still easily work out how fast to play this piece by using your watch. There are 60 seconds in a minute, so to make 120bpm (beats per minute) you need to play two crotchets per second. So, with some metronome markings, you can use your watch to get a feel for the tempo.

Be careful not to assume that metronome markings will always contain a crotchet. Faster markings may be given in minims, slower ones in quavers. For instance, the piece above could have been given this marking instead:

♩ = 60

The **tempo** is the same (each crotchet would still last for half a second) but the **beat** is different. You are now tapping your foot or clicking your metronome only once a second. In your head, you would count the bar as '1 and 2 and' rather than '1, 2, 3, 4'. For some tunes, counting in minims can help the tune flow more easily. We shall learn more about this in relation to $\frac{2}{2}$ time signatures later in the chapter.

Changing tempo

A piece need not be the same speed from beginning to end. When performing, you need to be able to respond correctly to tempo changes. If you are composing, you could do either of the following in your piece:

➢ Create a new section with a different tempo marking

➢ Increase or decrease the tempo for a short period of time.

If you create a new section with a different tempo marking you can simply insert one of the terms we learnt earlier above your music. Be careful not to do this too often as you may end up with a rather chopped-up piece!

For increasing or decreasing the tempo, there are some further terms which you need to know. Again, these are often given in Italian. The table below shows some of the most common terms you will see, along with their English translations and some common abbreviations.

Italian term	English translation
Meno mosso	Less movement
Più mosso	More movement
Ritenuto	Slow down immediately
Rallentando (rall.)	Slow down
Ritardando (rit.)	Slow down gradually
Accelerando (accel.)	Gradually increase the speed
A tempo	Back in tempo
Tempo primo	Return to the original speed of the piece (perhaps after a section of contrasting speed).

The following tune has been given lots of tempo instructions, far more than you would really want in a piece, but it's a useful practice exercise. Have a go at playing it and following all the tempo markings.

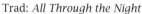

Trad: *All Through the Night*

If used in moderation, these kinds of tempo changes can make a piece more expressive: you could try using some in your own composition.

$\frac{2}{2}$, $\frac{3}{2}$ and cut-C time signatures

So far we have looked at melodies where the beat has been a crotchet. Sometimes it is more effective to count in minims, particularly if many of the note values used are themselves minims and crotchets. This helps to keep the beat flowing. If you counted the following piece in crotchets, it would feel rather tedious!

Byrd: Pavane

This piece has a time signature of $\frac{2}{2}$. This means you should count **two minims per bar** (rather than four crotchets, as you would in $\frac{4}{4}$). In both $\frac{2}{2}$ and $\frac{4}{4}$ the bars add up in the same way, but the feel of the beat is different.

A Pavane is a formal dance from the 16th century. A lot of music from the Elizabethan period is counted in minims. A Pavane in $\frac{2}{2}$, like the one above, was often followed by a Galliard in $\frac{3}{2}$.

Byrd: Galliard

While $\frac{2}{2}$ means 'count two minim beats in a bar', $\frac{3}{2}$ means 'count three minim beats in a bar'. This gives each piece a different feel for dancing.

In the same way as $\frac{4}{4}$ can be written as **C**, $\frac{2}{2}$ can be written as **¢**.

This is known as a **cut-C time signature**. When you see this, you should try to count the beat in minims.

Try playing the following tune:

Trad: *Hava Nagila*

This needs to be played quite fast and if you counted in crotchets the piece would probably end up being far too slow. Try counting the beat in minims and the tune should come to life.

The cut-C time signature is used a lot in musicals and 'songs from the shows', for example in Gershwin's **A Foggy Day.**

Exercise 1

In the tune below, some of the bar lines are missing. Add them in and have a go at playing the tune. The first bar line has been given, to show the anacrusis. Remember that the final bar will be incomplete in order to balance this anacrusic start.

Janequin: *La Bataille de Marignan*

Et o - res si bien é - cou - tez Des coups ru - és de tous cô - tés,

Compound time signatures

In the time signatures we have seen so far, we have been counting beats in crotchets or minims. These are known as simple time signatures. However, you will also see pieces that have a time signature of $\frac{6}{8}$. Have a look at the medieval song the Reading Rota, also known as *Sumer is Icumen In* below. Try humming it and tapping your foot at the same time. How many times in each bar do you tap your foot?

Anon: *Reading Rota*

> Dance forms such as the Gigue (or Jig), frequently used by 18th-century composers such as J S Bach, also use compound time.

You should find that there are two foot taps in every bar. This is because the beats are not counted in crotchets (as in $\frac{4}{4}$) but in **dotted crotchets**.

A dotted crotchet is worth three quavers. Two dotted crotchets add up to six quavers, hence the time signature $\frac{6}{8}$.

In the hymn above, each bar can be divided into two halves, and each half contains three quavers. Try drawing a pencil line through the middle of each bar and you will see how they divide. Time signatures such as $\frac{6}{8}$ are known as **compound time**. The beat is a dotted crotchet.

In $\frac{6}{8}$, quavers are often grouped into threes as in bar 2 above, but they are not triplets. We will now look at how to count them.

Counting with compound time signatures

Both $\frac{3}{4}$ and $\frac{6}{8}$ use six quavers per bar. However, if we compare them side by side, we will see how they differ.

Here is a bar of $\frac{3}{4}$:

| Count | 1 | 2 | 3 | 1 | and | 2 | and | 3 | and |

Here is a bar of $\frac{6}{8}$:

| Count | 1 | 2 | 1 | and | a | 2 | and | a |

The $\frac{3}{4}$ bar has three beats, each of which can be divided into two quavers. To count this, you could say '**1** and **2** and **3** and…'

The $\frac{6}{8}$ bar has two dotted crotchet beats, each of which can be divided into three quavers. To count this, you could say '**1** and a **2** and a…'.

Another simple rule of thumb for compound time signatures is to divide the top number by three: this gives you the number of beats in the bar.

Try the following well-known $\frac{6}{8}$ tunes, so that you can get a good feel for this time signature.

Trad: *Irish Washerwoman Jig*

Trad: *For He's a Jolly Good Fellow*

Writing bars in compound time

When writing a melody in $\frac{6}{8}$ (compound time), make sure that:

➢ All your bars add up to six quavers (except where an anacrusis occurs – see Chapter 2)

➢ Rhythms are grouped into two dotted crotchet beats.

Groups of three quavers that add up to a dotted crotchet beat should be beamed together, as in the two pieces above.

So, this:    should be written as this:

Notes should not extend across the middle of the bar. Instead, they should be split into two notes with a tie.

So, this: 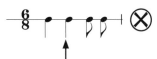   should be written as this:

This crotchet should be split into two quavers with a tie joining them together, so that the two dotted crotchet beats can still be seen clearly.

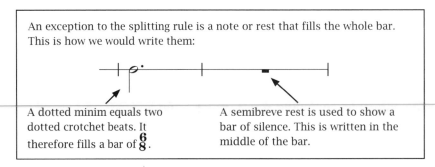

An exception to the splitting rule is a note or rest that fills the whole bar. This is how we would write them:

A dotted minim equals two dotted crotchet beats. It therefore fills a bar of $\frac{6}{8}$.

A semibreve rest is used to show a bar of silence. This is written in the middle of the bar.

Exercise 2
The following $\frac{6}{8}$ rhythms need bar lines adding to them. The first has been done for you.

Try to listen to the following pieces to hear $\frac{6}{8}$ (compound time) in action. A piece that is called Jig or Gigue is likely to be in compound time, like the *Irish Washerwoman Jig* on page 33.

> ➢ Gigue from Partita No 6 in E minor by J S Bach
>
> ➢ *Runaway* by The Corrs
>
> ➢ *The Archers* theme tune, as heard on Radio 4.

Time signatures

So far, we have looked at $\frac{2}{4}, \frac{3}{4}, \frac{4}{4}, \frac{2}{2}, \frac{3}{2}$ and $\frac{6}{8}$, but there are lots more time signatures you could create. Many of these are irregular, and there is no symmetrical way to organise the beat. Let's compare $\frac{4}{4}$ with an irregular time signature.

In $\frac{4}{4}$, the beats normally occur, with some natural stresses, as follows:

> Strong – weak – strong – weak.

If you decided to have five crotchet beats in a bar ($\frac{5}{4}$) there would be no way of dividing the beats into regular groups. You might end up with crotchet beats as follows:

> Strong – weak – weak – strong – weak.

Exercise 3

The following rhythms use irregular time signatures. Work out how many beats there are in each bar and then add a correct time signature at the beginning.

Exercise 4

You can change time signature as often as you like when you are composing. Simply insert a new time signature at the beginning of a bar, and it will last until your next time signature instruction. If a new time signature is required at the start of a stave, it should also appear at the end of the previous stave. The following rhythms keep changing their time signature. Insert time signatures as necessary. The second bar of the first one has been done for you.

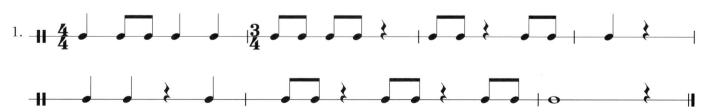

2.

3.

Exercise 5

The Russian composer Mussorgsky wrote a famous melody in his piece *Pictures at an Exhibition*, which keeps changing between different time signatures. Insert a correct time signature at the beginning of each bar, and then try to play the tune for yourself.

Mussorgsky: Extract from *Pictures at an Exhibition*

Try to listen to the following pieces which have irregular time signatures and think about what effect it has on the rhythm.

$\frac{5}{4}$	'Mars' from *The Planets* by Gustav Holst
$\frac{7}{4}$	*Money* by Pink Floyd.

Revision exercise

Complete the blanks in the text and tables below using words and symbols from the boxes:

tempo	pulse	Adagio	Allegro	Moderato	Andante	Largo
Vivace	Prestissimo	Presto	Meno mosso	Più mosso	Ritardando	Accelerando
A tempo	minims	$\frac{2}{2}$	$\frac{3}{2}$	$\frac{6}{8}$	compound	dotted crotchet

a) The _____ is what you tap your foot to. The _____ is how fast you tap your foot. Tempo markings are often given in Italian, though you will find them in other languages too.

b)

English translation	Italian term
Moderate speed	
Slow	
Slow and stately	
As fast as possible	
Quick	
Very quick	
Walking pace	
Lively	

Remember, if you want to give a more exact tempo instruction, you can write a metronome marking. You can change the tempo at any point in a piece.

c)

English translation	Italian term
More movement	
Less movement	
Slow down gradually	
Back in tempo	
Gradually increase the speed	

d) A time signature of $\frac{2}{2}$ tells us that the beat should be counted in _____.

If you want a piece with a beat of three minims per bar, then you should use a time signature of _____.

A cut-C time signature can be used instead of _____.

A Jig will often have a time signature of _____.

This is known as a_____time signature, where the beat is a _____.

Keywords
Compound time signature, cut-C time signature, metronome marking, tempo.

4. Scales and key signatures

We use many types of scale in music. Scales can be played on their own, or the notes from scales can be used to make melodies, chords and accompaniments.

In each of the scales that we shall look at in this chapter, the lowest and highest note of the scale has the same letter name. For example, if you look at the dorian mode below, you will see it starts on a low D, goes up to a high D and then goes back to a low D. If you look on a keyboard, you will see that there are eight consecutive white notes between a low D and a high D (counting the lower D as the first note). This is called an **octave**.

When writing or playing scales, we can choose either the **ascending** (going up) or **descending** (going down) form of the scale. Most scales use the same notes ascending and descending, but there are some scales that use notes when ascending that are different from those they use when descending. A scale can be played starting on any note and they use different combinations of naturals, sharps and flats.

Modes

Modes are scales which are often used in folk music and jazz, but they can also be found in pop and classical music. Two common modes that you are likely to come across are the **dorian mode** and the **aeolian mode**. Here is the dorian mode:

And here is the aeolian mode:

Both the dorian mode and aeolian mode can be played using only white notes on the keyboard. Try playing *What shall We do with a Drunken Sailor?* which uses the dorian mode:

Trad: *What Shall We do with a Drunken Sailor?*

Now try playing the opening *Star of the County Down* which uses the aeolian mode:

Trad: *Star of the County Down*

Intervals in scales

An **interval** is a gap between two notes.

Each mode has a specific pattern of intervals. Have a look at the interval patterns for the dorian and aeolian modes below (T = tone, ST = semitone). Remember to look at the gap *between* the notes to work out the intervals. Because there are eight notes in the scale, we have seven intervals:

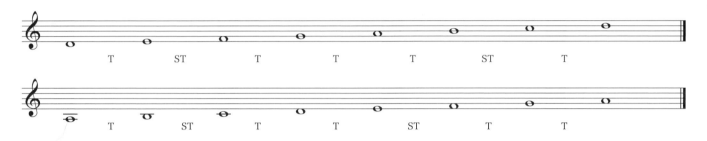

> Remember, the smallest interval between two notes on a keyboard is a semitone (for instance, A – B♭ or B – C). A tone is two semitones (for instance, A – B, or B – C♯).

So, if we start on D and play T - ST - T - T - T - ST - T we play a dorian mode.

However, if we start on D and play T - T - ST - T - T - T - ST we play a different type of scale - a **major scale**. Major scales always have a pattern of *consecutive* letter names, regardless of the sharps or flats they use.

So, the notes of D major are: D E F♯ G A B C♯ D

and not: D E G♭ G A B D♭ D

If you then reverse the interval pattern and go back down to the lower D (ST - T - T - T - ST - T - T), you will have played one octave of D major, ascending and descending:

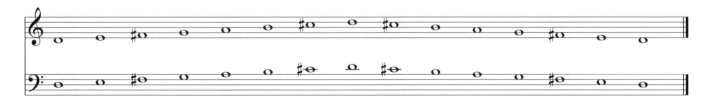

Major scales are always named after the note they start on, so the major scale starting on D is called D major. The starting note is also called the **tonic**. The major scale which starts on C is called C major and its tonic is C, the major scale which starts on F♯ is called F♯ major and its tonic is F♯, and so on.

Major scales

We can take the sequence of intervals T - T - ST - T - T - T - ST and play major scales starting on other notes. Try playing major scales starting on C, F, G, B♭, A and E♭.

Exercise 1

Here are a set of major scales written down without accidentals. Add any necessary sharps or flats to make them sound correct. Follow the interval pattern T - T - ST - T - T - T - ST for each scale.

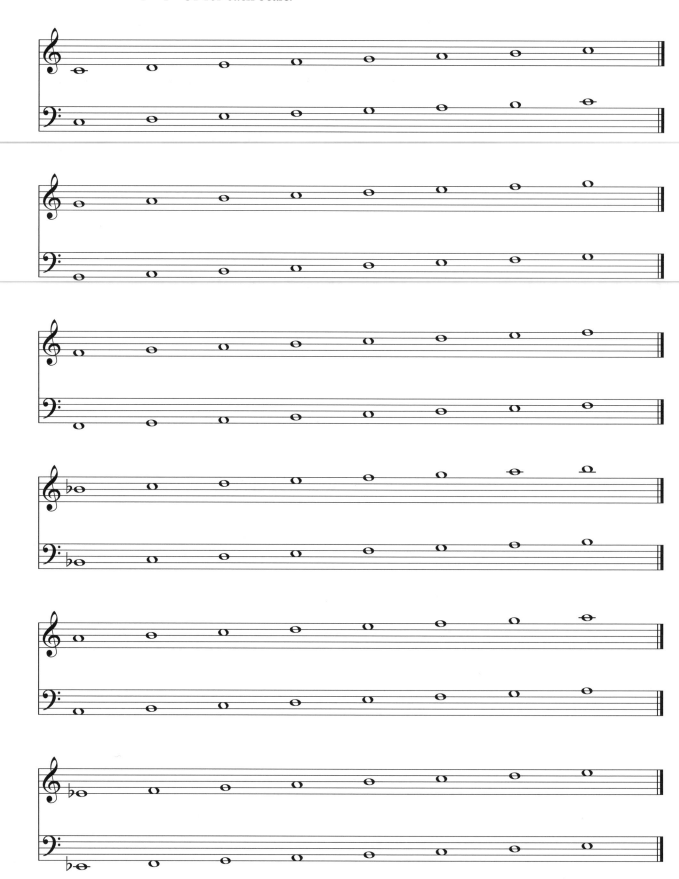

Key signatures

If a tune uses the notes of a particular scale, and uses its tonic as a 'home' note, then we say that the tune is **in the key** of that scale. So a tune that uses the notes of C major, with C as the home note, is in the key of C major. Similarly, a tune that uses the notes of F major, with F as the home note, is in the key of F major, and so on.

If we play the opening of *Somewhere over the Rainbow* in C major, we use all of the notes from the scale of C major, and we start and end on the tonic note (C). The tune is therefore in the key of C major and, if we play it on a keyboard, we use only the white notes:

Arlen: *Somewhere Over the Rainbow*

If we start *Somewhere over the Rainbow* on G, then we need to include F♯, in order to make the tune sound correct, and now it is in G Major:

As we discussed in Chapter 2, to save writing a sharp against every F in the music, we can place it at the start of the stave as a **key signature**:

The F♯ in the key signature lasts throughout the music, and so you play F♯ in bar 2 and bar 7. The sharps or flats that you use to write down a major scale become the key signature for any piece of music written in that key. Recognising the key signature of major keys will help you when reading music, as you will know which set of notes the tune is using.

We can also write scales using key signatures. Here are G major and F major written with key signatures (so we don't need to write sharps or flats against the appropriate notes).

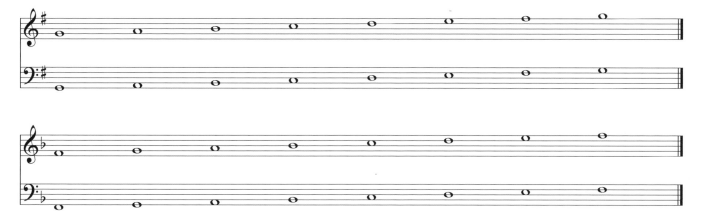

Exercise 2

Play ascending scales of D major, A major, B♭ major and E♭ major, and write them below with key signatures.

Writing key signatures on the stave

As well as needing to know which sharps and flats belong in the key signatures for different major scales, we also need to know where to write them on the stave *and in what order* (see page 48). In the treble clef sharps are written like this:

This is how they are written in the bass clef:

This is how flats are written in the treble clef:

This is how they are written in the bass clef:

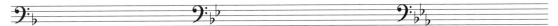

Minor scales

Like major scales, the starting note of any minor scale is called the tonic and it gives the scale its name. Minor scales also have a pattern of consecutive letter names, regardless of the sharps, flats and naturals that are used. As we shall see below, every minor scale is related to a major scale, with which it shares a key signature.

There are two types of minor scale, the **harmonic minor** and the **melodic minor**. We will look at the harmonic minor first.

Harmonic minor scales

We can work out a harmonic minor scale from its **relative major**. For instance, let's start with G major:

Minor scales start on note 6 of their related major scale. In the key of G major, note 6 is E, so the **relative minor** of G major is E minor. Another way that you can work out the starting note of the minor scale is by **going down three semitones** from the starting note of the major scale (so, G♮ – F♯, F♯ – F♮, F♮ – E♮).

Now play an octave of notes starting on E using the notes from the G major scale, like this:

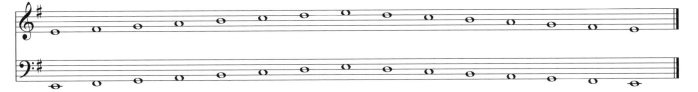

Now, raise the **seventh** note of this new scale so that there is a semitone between notes 7 and 8, as in a major scale. The notes of your new scale should now be:

E F♯ G A B C D♯ E (ascending) and E D♯ C B A G F♯ E (descending).

This is called the E harmonic minor scale.

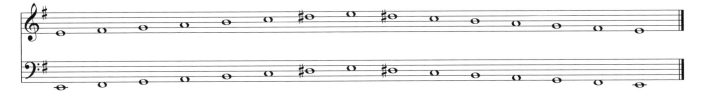

So, we can say that the key of E minor is the **relative minor** of the key of G major and, conversely, G major is the **relative major** of E minor.

Try playing this traditional Irish melody, *The King of the Fairies*, which is in E minor:

Trad: *The King of the Fairies*

Exercise 3

Write the relative harmonic minor of C major on the blank stave below.

Remember:

➢ The starting note is note 6 of the C major scale (so this isn't C minor!)

➢ You need to write an octave of notes starting on this note, using the same notes as the C major scale

➢ Raise the seventh note of this new scale so that there is a semitone between notes 7 and 8.

Now try writing out the relative harmonic minor scales of D major, A major, F major, Bb major and Eb major below. Don't forget to include the key signature in each case, which is the same as for the relative major.

Melodic minor scales

Most tunes using minor scales use the **melodic** minor scale. This scale starts like the harmonic minor, but note 6 is different, and it may surprise you that the descending form of the scale is different from the ascending form.

Here is C major, starting and finishing on note 6 (A):

To turn this into A melodic minor (C major's relative melodic minor, remember) we raise note 6 and note 7 by a *semitone* in the ascending form of the scale, and then lower both note 6 and note 7 back again by a *semitone* in the descending form of the scale, like this:

Now try writing E melodic minor below.

Don't forget the key signature

You should have E F(♯)G A B C♯ D♯ E (ascending) and E D♮ C♮ B A G F(♯) E (descending).

Exercise 4

Now have a go at writing the melodic minor scales of B minor, F♯ minor, D minor, G minor and C minor on the staves below.

When tunes are made from a melodic minor scale, the composer generally uses the ascending form of the scale when the melody rises and the descending form of the scale when the melody falls. Here is *David of the White Rock*, which is in E minor:

Trad: *David of the White Rock*

Here is the music for a verse from *We Three Kings*, which is in A minor:

Hopkins: *We Three Kings*

As *We Three Kings* uses the descending form of the melodic minor scale throughout, it is also using the notes of the aeolian mode. Go back and reread the beginning of the chapter if confused.

Unlike scales, tunes based on a minor scale do not have to use the raised versions of notes 6 and 7 when ascending, and the lowered versions when descending. Composers can choose to do the opposite, and raise notes 6 and 7 in a descending tune and lower them in an ascending tune.

Once you are familiar with the dorian mode and the aeolian mode, major scales and minor scales, you can try them out on a variety of starting notes.

Going further with modes

If you take the interval pattern of the dorian mode (T - ST - T - T - T - ST - T ascending) and use a different starting note, then you can make different versions of the dorian mode. If we start the dorian mode on G, it will be called G dorian:

G dorian (dorian mode starting on G)

Here is *Noel Nouvelet (Now the Green Blade Riseth)* using notes from the G dorian mode:

Trad: *Noel Nouvelet*

Moving a mode to a new starting note is called **transposing** (we will be looking at this in more detail in Chapter 7). We can also transpose the aeolian mode to start on G. This is called the G aeolian scale:

G aeolian (aeolian mode starting on G)

The aeolian mode is also called the natural minor

Notice that G aeolian is very similar to G minor, so we can use the same key signature as G minor for this scale and any tunes written using G aeolian, such as *Moondance* by Van Morrison.

Going further with major scales

You can play a major scale starting on any note. Pick a note and follow the T - T - ST - T - T - T - ST pattern until you reach the same letter name an octave higher. Write down the order of notes in each major scale, making sure that you name the notes using consecutive letter names, and note any sharps or flats. Once you've mastered a major scale, you can try composing a short tune in that key.

Going further with minor scales

You can play a minor scale starting on any note. Remember to follow these steps:

1. Pick a starting note, for example: F.

2. Work out the relative major by **going up three semitones** from the starting note of the minor scale: F♮ – G♭, G♭ – G, G – A♭. Note that the tonic note of the minor scale is always three letter names away from the relative major scale, so the relative major of F minor is A♭ major and not G♯ major.

3. Write out the key signature of this major scale, which is also the key signature of the new minor scale you're writing (see left).

4. Write out an octave of notes ascending and descending starting on the note you chose, using the key signature of the relative major.

5. Choose whether you want to write the harmonic or melodic minor version of the scale, and add the appropriate accidentals. F melodic minor has been written out below (so, notes 6 and 7 have been raised by a semitone ascending, and lowered again descending).

Going further with key signatures

If you play a major scale on every note, you will notice that there can be up to seven sharps or flats in a key signature.

Here is the conventional way of writing the key signature of C♯ major or A♯ minor, which has seven sharps (see left).

You can remember the order of the sharps as: **Father Charles Goes Down And Ends Battle**.

Here is the key signature of C♭ major or A♭ minor, which has seven flats (see left).

You can remember the order of the flats as: **Battle Ends And Down Goes Father Charles** (the same as the sharps but in reverse order).

To write key signatures with fewer than seven sharps or flats, draw in the number you need, always making sure to follow the order correctly, and of course drawing the sharps or flats in the right place on the stave.

Revision exercises

Complete this table, listing all the key signatures of the minor scales we have looked at in this chapter. Remember to write the key signature in the right places on the stave. Make sure you have written something in every box.

Name of minor scale	Name of relative major scale	Key signature	How the key signature is drawn on the stave
A minor		No sharps or flats	
		F♯	
B minor	D major		

F♯ minor	A major		
	F major	B♭	
	B♭ major		
C minor		B♭, E♭ and A♭	

Answer these multiple choice questions:

1. In a major scale you find intervals of:

    a) Tones and semitones

    b) Only tones

    c) Only semitones.

2. What is a semitone?

    a) The black note on a keyboard

    b) A sharp or a flat

    c) The smallest possible interval between two adjacent notes on a keyboard.

3. A tone is:

    a) A white note on a keyboard

    b) An interval of two semitones

    c) The starting note of a scale.

4. An ascending major scale uses the interval pattern of:

    a) ST – T – T – T – ST – T – T

    b) T – T – ST – T – T – T – ST

    c) T – ST – T – ST – T – ST – T.

5. The tonic note is:

    a) The first note of a major scale and of a minor scale

    b) The first note of a major scale only

    c) The first note of a minor scale only.

6. The tonic note of F♯ minor is:

    a) F♮

    b) F♯

    c) F♭.

7. Minor scales are called the relative minor of a major key when:

    a) They start on the same note

    b) They share the same key signature

    c) They sound the same.

8. The two types of minor scales are called:

    a) Harmonic and cadence

    b) Tonic and dominant

    c) Harmonic and melodic.

9. The interval between notes 7 and 8 of a harmonic minor scale is:

    a) A semitone

    b) A tone

    c) An octave.

10. Which of these statements is true about melodic minor scales?

    a) You raise notes 6 and 7 by a semitone in the ascending form of the scale and lower notes 6 and 7 back again by a semitone in the descending form of the scale

    b) You write sharps before notes 6 and 7 when the scale ascends and flats on notes 6 and 7 as the scale descends

    c) The notes are the same when the scale is ascending and descending.

5. Performance directions

So far, we've learnt how to write pitch, rhythm and tempo directions.

In addition to tempo, there are many other performance directions that composers can use to show how their music should be performed. It is the effect of these directions that can bring a piece of music to life

These two examples show the same melody. Look carefully at the differences in the way they are written.

Mendelssohn: *Song without Words*

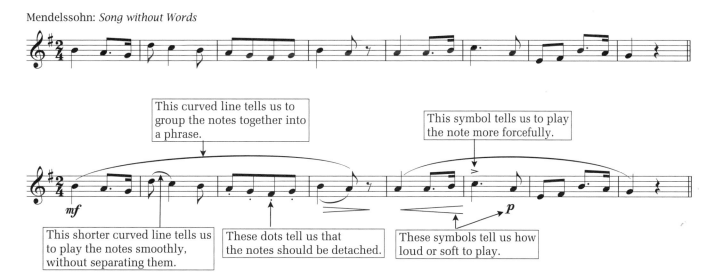

The two versions use exactly the same notes and rhythms, but the first tells us nothing about how to play them. We are not told anything about the **dynamics** (how loud or soft to play), or whether notes should be smooth or detached. All these things would have to be decided by the performer.

You can use performance directions for rehearsing (bar numbers and rehearsal figures), structure (repeat marks), loudness (dynamics) and smoothness (articulation). We shall now look at all of these in more detail.

Bar numbers and rehearsal figures

Bar numbers are used to find locations in a piece. These are particularly useful in rehearsing, especially if there are several people playing together. They help you all find the same place in the music, so that as you practise a difficult passage you can tell each other to 'start at bar 15'. This stops you from getting lost!

Bar numbers are often added every 5 or 10 bars, or at the beginning of each line of the stave, starting from the second line. Music software packages often automatically add bar numbers for you.

If a piece begins with an anacrusis (upbeat), then we count the first *complete* bar as 'bar 1'. We do not count the upbeat as a bar.

Pieces written for larger groups of players, such as orchestras, will often have **rehearsal letters**. Like bar numbers, these help all the players make sure they are playing the same section of music during rehearsing. Rehearsal letters follow the alphabet and are found inside a box. They usually appear at the start of new sections or phrases in the music. A conductor can then say 'play from letter A'.

In this tune, the bars are numbered at the start of the line and there is a rehearsal letter at bar 8.

Lennon/McCartney: *Yesterday*

Try playing the melody. This will also help you revise tied notes. Go back to Chapter 2 if you have forgotten about these.

What else do you notice about this melody? Using the bar numbers, you can see that bars 8–14 (starting at letter A) are identical to bars 1–7. As you are about to see, we needn't write out the music twice.

Repeat marks

Repeat marks can save time and space. They tell you to repeat a passage of music, i.e. to play it twice.

Look at the piece of music below. You will see that bars 5–8 have exactly the same notes and rhythm as bars 1–4.

Trad: *All Through the Night*

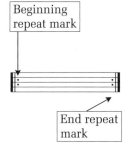

To save writing out the same music twice, the composer could use repeat marks. These look like this (see left).

Repeat marks go at the beginning and the end of the section of music you want repeating. However, if you are repeating back to the *start* of a piece, then you do not need a beginning repeat mark.

Here is the extract again, this time with repeat marks.

Repeat marks can also be used in longer pieces of music of all kinds if a section is intended to be heard twice.

Look at the folk tune below. Where are the repeat marks? Which sections do you need to play twice?

Trad: *One Hundred Pipers*

To perform this tune, you need to play:

➤ From the beginning to the first repeat mark

➤ The same again

➤ From the repeat mark to the end

➤ The same again.

You will see that repeat marks only mean one repeat. Otherwise, you would just keep playing bars 1-8 and never get to the second half of the tune!

Have a go at playing the folk tune. This is also a chance to revise the key signature of A major and compound time – the time signature is $\frac{6}{8}$ (see Chapter 3 if you need to remind yourself of this).

First and second time bars

Have a look at this melody. Where is the repeat mark?

You will see that the bar with the repeat mark also has a '1' over it. This is called the **first time bar**. You start by playing the tune from the beginning until you reach the repeat sign in the first time bar. This tells us to play the tune again from the beginning.

This time when you get to the end of bar 3, instead of playing bar 4 (the first time bar), you jump to the bar marked '2', the **second time bar**.

> The first time you play the tune, you play the first time bar.
>
> The second time you play the tune, you play the second time bar.

So, to perform this tune you would play:

➤ Bars 1, 2, 3, **4a**

➤ Bars 1, 2, 3, **4b**, 5, 6, 7, 8, 9, 10, 11, 12.

A note on bar numbers

First and second time bars do not have separate bar numbers. Instead, they are referred to as 'a' and 'b'. In the above extract, it is the fourth bar of the tune that is the first or second time bar (depending if you are playing it for the first or second time). The first time bar is therefore '4a', the second time bar is '4b'.

Try playing the melody above – it will help you practise moving between first and second time bars.

Da Capo and Dal Segno

These are special kinds of directions. They are sometimes difficult to follow and you need to stay completely on the ball to avoid getting lost!

Here are some essential vocabulary and symbols:

What you see	What it means
Da Capo (D.C.)	Go back to the beginning
Dal Segno (D.S.)	Go back to the sign, which looks like this: 𝄋
Fine	End here
Coda	A section of music to complete a piece (literally, 'tail' in Italian)
⊕	Cut to the coda when you reach this sign.

You will normally see a combination of these words. Two common combinations are:

What you see	What you should do
Da Capo al fine (D.C. al fine)	Go back to the beginning and play the piece again until you reach the word 'fine' (end)
Dal Segno al coda (D.S. al coda)	Go back to the sign and play until the coda symbol. Then jump to the coda and play it to finish the piece. This often happens in pop songs.

Da Capo al fine

You might use Da Capo al fine if you want the performer to play the first part of your piece again at the end.

Have a go at playing the following melody. The familiar tune will help you to tell if you've followed the instructions correctly!

Trad: *Twinkle Twinkle, Little Star*

You should have played:

➢ Bars 1–8

➢ Bars 1–4

Dal Segno al coda

You might use Dal Segno al coda if you want the performer to repeat an earlier part of your piece and then continue on to some new music to finish.

Have a go at playing the melody below. You should play until the words **D.S. al coda**. You then go back to the sign (𝄋) which is at the start of the first complete bar. You then continue to the coda symbol (𝄌) at the end of bar 6. At this point you jump to the coda and play the last two bars.

Trad: *Scotland the Brave*

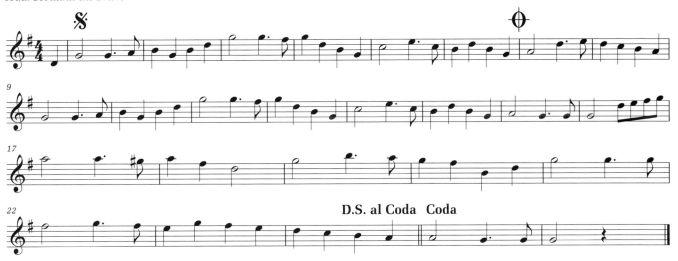

The correct sequence for this piece is as follows:

➢ Bars 1-24

➢ Bars 1-6

➢ Bars 25-26 (Coda.)

Dal Segno al coda is often used in pop songs when the verse or chorus normally repeats, but the last verse or chorus has a different ending, or there is some extra music to fade out.

Exercise 1

Look at *Away in a Manger* on page 19 and rewrite this on the stave below using first and second time bars. (Hint: you can have more than one bar grouped together as a first or second time bar!)

Exercise 2

Look at the complete melody of *For He's a Jolly Good Fellow* on page 31, and then add appropriate directions to the version below so that it will sound the same.

Dynamics (loud and soft)

Music would be boring if every single note was the same loudness: it would be like always shouting or always whispering. When playing or composing a piece sometimes you will want the music to be loud, and sometimes you will want it to be soft.

Dynamic markings tell you to vary the loudness of the music. They are normally shown as an Italian abbreviation or symbol:

What you see	What it means	How you should play
pp	Pianissimo	Very softly
p	Piano	Softly
mp	Mezzo piano	Fairly softly
mf	Mezzo forte	Fairly loudly
f	Forte	Loudly
ff	Fortissimo	Very loudly
cresc. or	Crescendo	Get louder gradually
dim. or	Diminuendo	Get softer gradually

These markings don't tell you exactly how loud or soft to play, but they give you a general idea. They are relative to one another – if you are told to play *f* you should be louder than when you played *mf* which should be louder than when you played *p*.

Listen to the range of dynamics in the following pieces:

➢ Opening of 'Mars' from *The Planets* by Holst (*f*)

➢ *Hard to Beat* by Hard-fi (*f*)

➢ Prelude No 15, *Raindrop*, by Chopin (*p*)

➢ *Boléro* by Ravel (one giant crescendo from start to finish!)

➢ 'O Fortuna' from *Carmina Burana* by Orff (sudden shifts from *ff* to *pp* to *ff* at the beginning)

➢ Symphony No 94, *Surprise*, 2nd movt by Haydn (sudden changes in dynamics).

For melody instruments on a single stave, dynamics are written under the notes they apply to. In a piano piece, they are usually written in between the two staves (see bar 1 below). The symbols for crescendo and diminuendo can be stretched out to show how long they should last for (see bar 2). You can also write *cresc.* or *dim.* under the note where you would like the crescendo or diminuendo to start (see bar 3).

In the above example, you would:

➢ Play loudly in bar 1

➢ Gradually get quieter throughout bar 2

➢ Gradually get louder throughout bar 3.

Play the following tune, paying special attention to the dynamics. Remember how the first and second time bars work too!

Work: *My Grandfather's Clock*

Now have another go at the tune and try making the different dynamics more extreme. Find out what is possible on your instrument!

Slurs, phrase marks and articulation

You can avoid confusing a **slur** with a **tie** by remembering that a tie joins together notes of the *same* pitch to make a longer note. A slur groups together notes of *different* pitch.

A **slur** is a curved line which is drawn over or underneath two or more notes. Slurs group notes of different pitch together. These notes should then be played **smoothly (legato)**. For wind instruments, this means that you only tongue the first note of the slur and don't breathe in the middle. For stringed instruments, this means you play all the notes with one bow stroke.

When two notes are joined together with a slur, think of them in the following way: a slight stress on the first note followed by a lighter, bouncier second note. Say the word 'Sunday' several times and you'll get a feel for the sound of a strong syllable joined to a lighter one.

Try playing the following melody which includes a number of slurs. This melody will also help you revise the smaller (semiquaver) note values, accidentals, and the first and second time repeats.

Brahms: Waltz

etc

Now look at the following melody:

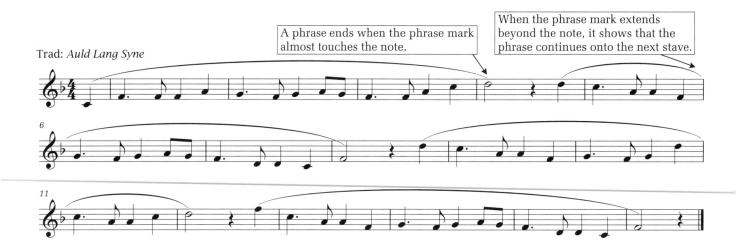

The melody is divided into four phrases, each shown by a long curved line called a **phrase mark**. Although they look like slurs, phrase marks group together longer musical ideas. Each phrase mark begins on the first note of the phrase and ends on the last one. Notice how some of the phrases continue from one stave to the next.

Phrase marks are a bit like punctuation in a book and show you how a piece breaks down into shorter units. Most importantly for wind players or singers, they tell you where to breathe! You would normally breathe at the end of a phrase, not in the middle of one.

The most common length for a musical phrase is 4 to 8 bars, especially in folk tunes or music by composers such as Mozart and Haydn. *Auld Lang Syne* divides neatly into four 16-beat phrases, each ending with a crotchet rest.

Exercise 3

Play through the following melody and then draw in the phrase marks, in the places where you think they make most musical sense:

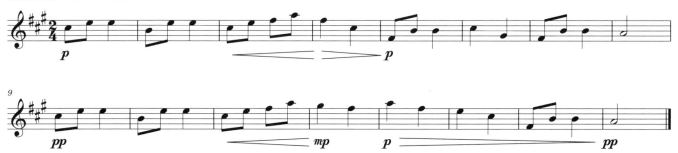

Staccatos and accents

While slurs and phrase marks are about playing smoothly, there are markings that tell us to play in a heavy or detached way.

An **accent** (›) tells us to play a note more loudly or emphasise it more.

A dot underneath or over a note (**staccato**) tells us that the note should be short and separated from the next note. On a keyboard, this means pressing and releasing the note as quickly as possible. Be careful not to speed up as you play staccato! Each note, however short, must still land on the right beat of the bar.

Both accents and staccato appear in the following piece:

Kabalevsky: Dance

If the note's stem goes upwards, the staccatos and accents go underneath the note. If the note's stem goes downwards, the staccatos and accents go above the note. This is so the staccatos and accents don't overlap with the stems and look messy.

Lyrics

Lyrics are the words to a song. When you write a song, it is important to match the words and music carefully, so that they make sense together.

To set words to music, the first task is to think about the rhythm of the words.

Words can be divided into **syllables**. It is the number and pattern of syllables in a word that gives it its rhythm. Words can have one, two, three or more syllables. With the examples below, try clapping to the words as you say them. You should find that the number of claps naturally corresponds to the number of syllables.

➢ Words with one syllable: 'dog', 'pen'

➢ Words with two syllables: 'colour', 'pattern' (clap: co-lour; pat-tern)

➢ Words with three syllables: 'computer', 'conductor' (clap: com-pu-ter; con-duc-tor).

Try clapping to these words as you say them: 'rhythm', 'party', 'Mozart', 'potato', 'motorway', 'photography'. How many syllables does each one have?

In English words and sentences, some syllables are naturally more emphasised than others.

To set words to music, we need to decide which syllables are the strong ones – that is, the ones that are emphasised or stressed.

Try reading these lyrics:

> On the first day of Christmas
> My true love gave to me:
> A partridge in a pear tree.
>
> On the second day of Christmas
> My true love gave to me:
> Two turtle doves and
> A partridge in a pear tree.

Read the words to yourself several times. Which syllables are naturally stressed? Underline the strong syllables.

Now look at the words together with the music, shown overleaf. The words are written underneath the notes, so that the singer can see the lyrics and the music at the same time. Underline the strong syllables again.

What do you notice about where they fall in the music?

Trad: *The Twelve Days of Christmas*

On the first day of Christ-mas my true love sent to me, A par-tridge__ in a pear tree. On the
sec-ond day of Christ-mas my true love gave to me, Two tur-tle doves and a par-tridge in a pear tree.

You will see that the strong syllables all fall at the beginning of a bar. This helps the words fit to the music.

Because the strong syllables are stressed in words, they need to be stressed in the music too.

As the first beat of a bar is usually stressed, putting a strong syllable there means that the singer will naturally put the stress in the right place. The words and music are doing the same thing.

You may notice a number of other things about the way the notes and the words are written. Let's look at these in turn:

Christ - mas   my

Each note in a song can only have one syllable underneath it. 'Christmas' is two syllables ('Christ – mas'), so it needs two notes. To write words in a vocal score, we break each word into syllables and put a hyphen ('-') between them.

par - tridge___

Each syllable, however, can have as many notes as you like. Here the syllable 'tridge' from 'partridge' is set to two notes in the melody. One syllable with more than one note is called a **melisma**. A melisma often highlights an important word. Think of the chorus of the carol *Ding Dong Merrily on High*. The word 'Gloria' lasts for several bars, with many notes sung to the syllable 'Glor'. You can join the notes of the melisma together with a slur.

Finally, notice that the second verse uses basically the same tune but with a few changes to fit the words.

For example, this: becomes this:

On   the   first   day   of   On   the   sec - ond   day   of

An extra note has been added into the second verse, because the word 'second' has two syllables. This is possible as long as the stress patterns of the words still fit the music.

<table>
<tr><td>

Verses

In a song where the same music repeats for each verse, the lyrics for subsequent verses can be written under the previous one. Alternatively, you can write the extra verses as paragraphs under your music at the end.

</td></tr>
</table>

Exercise 4

Underline the strong syllables in the following lyrics.

One, two, buckle my shoe
Three, four, shut the door
Five, six, pick up sticks
Seven, eight, lay them straight.

There was a Young Lady whose eyes,
Were unique as to colour and size;
When she opened them wide,
People all turned aside,
And started away in surprise.
Edward Lear

Exercise 5

Now try writing melodies for them. Remember to make sure the strong syllable falls at the beginning of the bar or on a strong beat.

Exercise 6

Have another look at the piece called Minuet on page 19. Rewrite this using any of the following: repeat bars, first and second time bars, coda.

Exercise 7

The following extract contains a number of performance directions, each labelled with a letter. For each symbol, say what it is or what it is short for, and what it tells you to do in a performance. The first one has been done for you.

Schubert: Scherzo

Keywords
Accent, articulation, bar numbers, coda, Da Capo, Dal Segno, dynamics, fine, first and second time bars, lyrics, melisma, performance directions, phrase marks, rehearsal letters, repeat marks, slur, staccato, syllable, verse.

Letter	What it is, or what it is short for	What it tells you to do
A	Pianissimo	Play very softly
B		
C		
D		
E		
F		
G		
H		

6. Chords: choosing which notes fit together

Chords are created by playing two or more notes together. When you write them down, they must line up vertically on the stave. You can play chords on instruments such as the piano and guitar, because these instruments can play more than one note at a time.

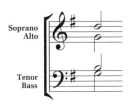

However, to play a chord using single-line instruments, such as the flute or trombone, or voices, you need a group of performers to play or sing one note each (see left):

The combination of different chords that composers use in their music is called harmony. It is **harmony** that makes music sound interesting. We use harmony to make melodies, accompaniments and backing tracks, and also to create certain moods and atmospheres.

Triads

The triad is one of the most useful chords available to us in music. The two most common types of triad are major and minor. A major or minor triad is a chord with three different notes:

They can be written in any clef and can have naturals and sharps, or naturals and flats on any of the three notes. Major and minor triads can be written or built on any note.

Major and minor triads

To create a major triad, we use notes 1, 3 and 5 of a major scale, and name the triad after note 1. So, a D major triad uses notes 1, 3 and 5 of a D major scale (D F♯ A):

In a major triad, the interval between notes 1 and 3 (D and F♯) is a **major 3rd.**

Each note in the triad is given a special name. Counting up from the bottom, note 1 (D) of the triad is called the root, note 3 (F♯) is called the 3rd and note 5 (A) is called the 5th:

A major 3rd is an interval of four semitones

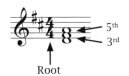

When a triad is written in this way, it is in **root position**, because the lowest sounding note is also the root of the chord. This D major triad is also written in **close position**, with the notes of the triad as close together as possible on the stave. The notes of a triad written in root and close position will have alternate letter names.

A minor triad is notes 1, 3 and 5 of a minor scale, and is also called after note number 1. To make a D minor triad, we take notes 1, 3 and 5 of a D minor scale (D F A). The interval between notes 1 and 3 (D and F) is a **minor 3rd**:

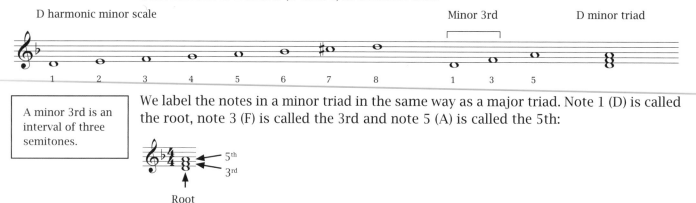

| A minor 3rd is an interval of three semitones. |

We label the notes in a minor triad in the same way as a major triad. Note 1 (D) is called the root, note 3 (F) is called the 3rd and note 5 (A) is called the 5th:

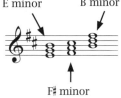

Chords and key signatures

If we use the notes of the D major scale, we can make three different major triads:

E minor   B minor

D major   G major   A major

We can also make three different minor triads (see left).

F♯ minor

We are able to do this because D major shares some of its notes with the notes of other major and minor scales. For example, the notes in a G major triad (G B D) are notes 1, 3, 5 of a G major scale, and also notes 4, 6, 8 of a D major scale. The notes in an E minor triad (E G B) are notes 1, 3, 5 of an E minor scale, and also notes 2, 4, 6 of a D major scale. It doesn't matter that both G major and E minor have different key signatures (F♯) to D major (F♯, C♯). Think of the root note of a major or minor triad as being note 1 of the major or minor scale that starts on that note, regardless of the key of the music.

Arpeggios

If you play the notes of a major or minor triad as a pattern of separate notes then you play arpeggios or broken chords, as shown below:

This bar uses notes from the D major triad

This bar uses notes from the A major triad

Exercise 1

To tell the difference between major and minor triads, think of the first three notes of the scale that starts on the triad's root note. If the 3rd of the triad is the third note of the major scale it is a major triad; if it is the third note of the minor scale, the triad is minor.

Look at triad (a) above. Reading up from the root, it is made up of the notes G B D, so we know that it is either a G major or G minor triad. We know that notes 1–3 of G major are G A B, whereas notes 1–3 of G minor are G A B♭, so we, looking at notes in the middle of the triad, can tell that this is a G major triad.

Now try to name triads (b), (c) and (d) above. Here are notes 1–3 of the major and minor scales that start on each of the root notes, to help you:

> Triad (b): Notes 1–3 of F♯ major are F♯ G♯ A♯, notes 1–3 of F♯ minor are F♯ G♯ A

> Triad (c): Notes 1–3 of F major are F G A, notes 1–3 of F minor are F G A♭

> Triad (d): Notes 1–3 of C major are C D E, notes 1–3 of C minor are C D E♭.

Exercise 2

Now name the following triads. Remember to work out notes 1–3 of the major and minor scales which start on the root notes of each one.

Exercise 3

Now draw in the notes of the following chords, as root position and close position major and minor triads.

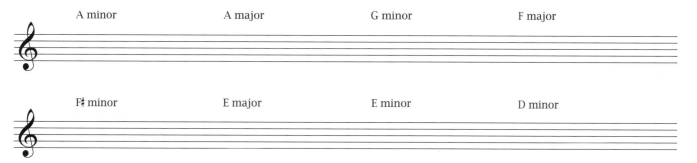

Open position triads

A D minor triad can be written in several different ways:

Each of the above are D minor triads, because they only contain the notes of a D minor triad (D F A) and have the root of the triad (D) as the lowest-sounding note. However, while version (a) is written in close position (with the notes as close as possible on the stave), versions (b) and (c) are written in open position, with the 3rd and 5th of the triad (F and A) written at other pitches. Notice that the 3rd and 5th can be written in a different order. Version (b) of the D minor triad is D A F.

Exercise 4

Identify the following triads which are written in open position. First, start by identifying the notes in the triad, and then reorder them into a close position triad (you might like to do this on a spare piece of paper). Remember that a close position triad will have alternate letter names, and the lowest sounding note will be the root of the triad. Then check the interval between the root and the 3rd of the triad to identify whether it is a major or a minor triad.

In the Remember box:

Remember

A triad is made of tonic, third and fifth degrees (notes 1, 3 and 5) of a scale.

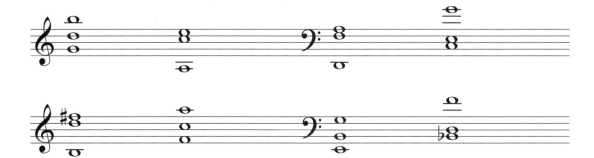

Reading chords on more than one stave

Chords can be written across several staves. To read a chord written like this, first identify the letter names of each note, writing them on the music if necessary. Write the letter names of the notes in the chord on a spare piece of paper, and cross out any that are repeated. Then, reorder the letter names to make a root position and close position triad (it will have alternating letter names). The lowest sounding note will be the root of this triad. Finally, check whether the interval between the root and the 3rd is that of a major or minor key, to see whether you have a major or minor triad.

The notes in the chord to the left (reading from the bottom up) are D, D, A and F♯. Ignoring the repeated letters, this gives us: D, A and F♯. Reordering these notes into a root position, close position triad gives us D F♯ A. The root of the chord is D, so this will be a D major or D minor triad. The interval between D and F♯ is a major 3rd, so we know that this is a D major triad.

Exercise 5

Write in the names of the following chords.

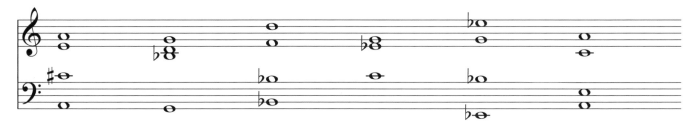

Chord symbols

Chord symbols are letters (sometimes with numerals or other symbols) used as shorthand to describe chords. They are often used in pop, rock and jazz. Some musicians play from a lead sheet which contains the melody or sometimes just the lyrics of a song with chord symbols written above the music.

All chord symbols start with a capital letter, sometimes with a sharp or flat attached. This tells you the root of the chord. So the chord symbol 'F' is a triad that starts on an F, and the chord symbol 'F♯' is a triad that starts on the note F♯. If there is a lower case 'm' after the capital letter, this means that it is a minor triad, so 'F♯m' is an F♯ minor triad (F♯ A C♯). Sometimes a minor triad can be written 'F♯-' or 'F♯mi' or 'F♯min'. If there is only a capital letter, then it is a major triad, so 'F' is a major triad (F A C).

Chord symbols are often shown above the melody in a printed song. Here is the opening of *Catch a Falling Star*.

The performer reads the chord symbols and plays an accompaniment based on the chords given. Some performers might sing the melody at the same time as playing the chords.

Harmony and non-harmony notes

In *Catch a Falling Star* you will notice that the melody uses some notes that belong to a G major triad (G B D), and other notes that do not. The notes in the melody that belong to the chord being used to accompany the song are called **harmony notes**. The other notes, each marked with an arrow below, are called **non-harmony notes**.

Provided non-harmony notes fall on a weak beat in the bar (in this case, beat 4), it does not matter if they do not fit with the chord. However, there should always be more harmony notes than non-harmony notes in each bar, so that the chords that are played in the accompaniment sound like they fit with the melody.

A commonly occuring non harmony note is a **passing note** which creates a link between two harmony notes in a melody, a 3rd apart. Examples can be found on page 72, *Four Chord Bragg*.

Roman numerals

We can also use a system of Roman numerals to label chords. If we build a triad on every note in a major scale, we can label them with Roman numerals and write the name of the tonic note at the start. We use uppercase Roman numerals for major triads and lower case for minor triads. Below you can see triads on every note of a D major scale, labelled with Roman numerals (chord *vii* is neither major nor minor – see page 68):

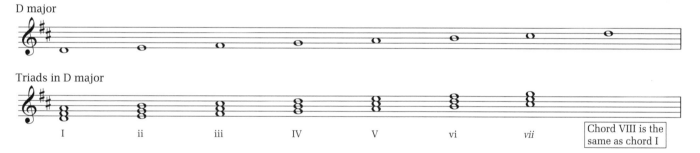

We can do the same in a minor key. Notice that we have used the harmonic minor scale to make chords in a minor key. Below are triads on every note in a D minor scale, labelled with Roman numerals (chords *ii*, *III* and *vii* are neither major nor minor – see page 68):

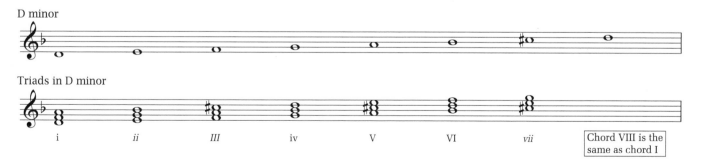

Triads in D major

We can also give each note and triad in the scale a name, like this:

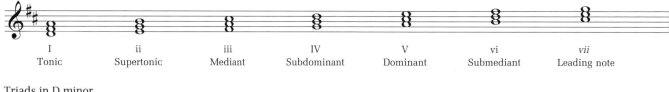

I	ii	iii	IV	V	vi	vii
Tonic	Supertonic	Mediant	Subdominant	Dominant	Submediant	Leading note

Triads in D minor

i	ii	III	iv	V	VI	vii
Tonic	Supertonic	Mediant	Subdominant	Dominant	Submediant	Leading note

So, in both major and minor keys, chord I can also be called the tonic chord, chord ii can be called the supertonic chord, and so on. We can also give two different names to the chords we use. Above, you can see that the D major triad can be called 'D', and also chord I of D major; the E minor triad can be called 'Em' and also chord ii of D major, and so on. When we are using roman numerals to label chords, we start by identifying the key and then give the chord numbers.

In the piece below, *Four Chord Brag*, the chords are labelled using roman numerals and chord symbols, and the extra stave below the piano part shows the harmony as block chords.

Diminished and augmented triads

Chord *vii* in both major and minor keys, and chord *ii* in a minor key are called diminished triads. Chord *III* in a minor key is called an augmented triad. We won't be looking at these types of triads in this chapter.

Four Chord Brag

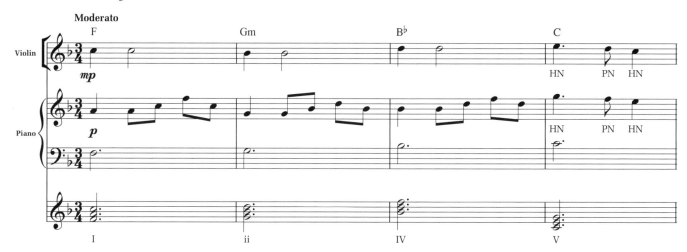

The last bar in *Four Chord Brag* contains harmony notes and non-harmony notes in the violin part and the right hand (treble stave) of the piano. These kind of non-harmony notes are called passing notes because they pass between two harmony notes which are a 3rd apart. Notice how the harmony notes are on the beat, and the passing notes are off the beat.

Inverted triads

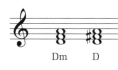

So far, we have discussed major and minor triads in root position, that is, with the root as the lowest sounding note, as on the left.

We can also put the 3rd or the 5th as the lowest sounding note. When the 3rd is the lowest sounding note, the triad is in its **first inversion**. When the 5th is the lowest sounding note, the triad is in its **second inversion**. We are using the same pitches, but with different notes as the lowest sounding note.

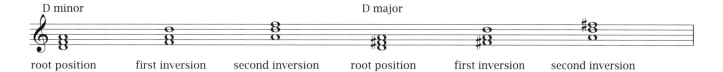

The inverted triads above are written in close position, with the notes as close together as possible on the stave.

Exercise 6

Write in the first and second inversions of the following triads. Write them as close position triads, making sure that the notes are as close together as possible on the stave. (Hint: you can always write these chords an octave higher or lower to avoid using too many leger lines.)

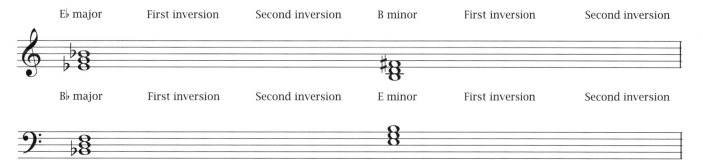

Exercise 7

Identify the following inverted triads. In each case, write the name of the triad, and the inversion. To do this, you need to:

> ➤ Identify the notes in the triad and then rearrange them into root position – this will give you the root and the name of the chord

> ➤ Check the interval between the root and the third to see whether this is a major or minor triad

> ➤ Look back at the way the chord was originally written and identify whether the lowest sounding note is the root, the third or the fifth – this will tell you which inversion the triad is in.

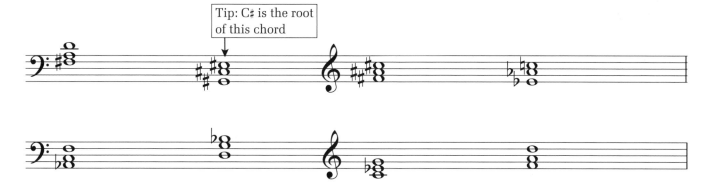

If we are going to write the chord across several staves, then we need to do two things:

> ➤ Name the notes being played, so that we can identify what triad it is

> ➤ Spot the lowest-sounding note and identify which note in the triad it is (this will tell us whether the triad is being played in root position, first inversion or second inversion).

SATB refers to the soprano, alto, tenor and bass parts often found in choral music.

Here is the opening of Tallis' Canon, written for an SATB choir. The chords are also written in root position, close position triads on the stave below.

The first two chords are G major (G B D), but the second chord is in first inversion, because the 3rd of the triad (B) is the lowest sounding note.

The third chord is a D major triad in second inversion, because the fifth of the triad (A) is the lowest sounding note.

You will also notice that when a triad, which has three notes, is written as a chord with more than three notes, as in the example left, then some of the notes have to be doubled, or performed by two or more different parts. Often, it is the root of the chord that is doubled, which is why the first chord is sung as G (bass) B (tenor) D (alto) and G (soprano).

If you are using chord symbols, then you can indicate that a chord is inverted by writing a 'slash chord' such as C/E, which means play a C major triad with E in the bass. If you are using Roman numerals, then you can indicate the chord inversions by using 'b' for a first inversion and 'c' for a second inversion, for example: Ib and Ic. Here is some more of Tallis' Canon in which you can see these symbols used:

Tallis: Canon

Cadences

A cadence can be formed by the last two chords of a musical phrase. You might like to think of a cadence as musical punctuation. We use a particular combination of chords to create different types of cadences, according to the effect we want to create, and the notes in the melody. A piece of music can have many cadences in it.

To create a finished, 'full stop' effect we can use a **perfect cadence** or a **plagal cadence**. The perfect cadence is chord V (dominant) followed by chord I (tonic). Here is the opening of Tallis' Canon, again with the harmony written in as block chords in the lowest stave.

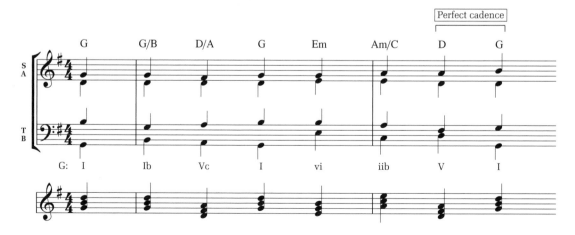

Notice that the two chords that make up the cadence are always next to each other. We can rewrite the music to end with a plagal cadence, which is chord IV (subdominant) followed by chord I (tonic).

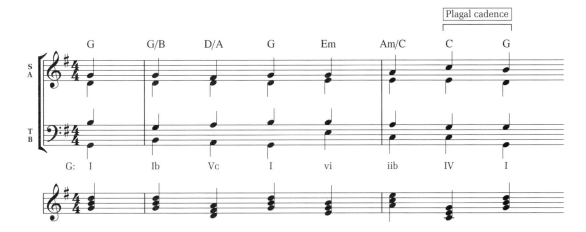

To create a half-finished, 'comma' effect we can use an **imperfect cadence**. An imperfect cadence always has chord V (dominant) as its second chord, and commonly has chord I (tonic), chord ii (supertonic), or chord IV (subdominant) as the first chord. Here is another way we can rewrite this piece to end with an imperfect cadence:

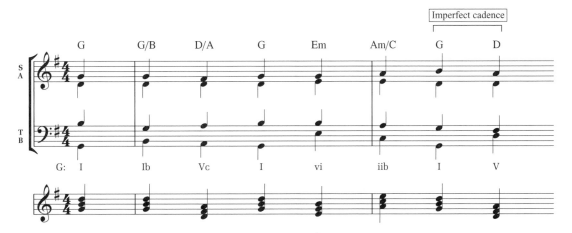

To create a surprise or 'exclamation mark' effect we can use an **interrupted cadence**. An interrupted cadence is chord V (dominant) followed by almost any chord other than the tonic chord. In this example, we are using chord V (dominant) followed by chord vi (submediant):

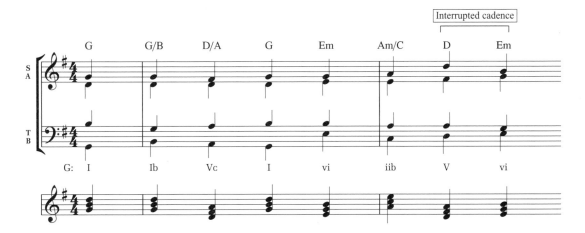

Turning chords into an accompaniment or backing

Composers use a wide range of different techniques to make an accompaniment from chords, and these all look different when they are written down.

We'll now look at some common accompaniment styles.

Block chords

The notes of each chord are all played together. Block chords can be repeated, as in the opening of *Bohemian Rhapsody* by Queen, or played as long notes.

Here is *Four Chord Brag* with an accompaniment made from block chords. Notice that the tune contains **passing notes** in bars 4 and 8, and the accompaniment includes triads in inversion.

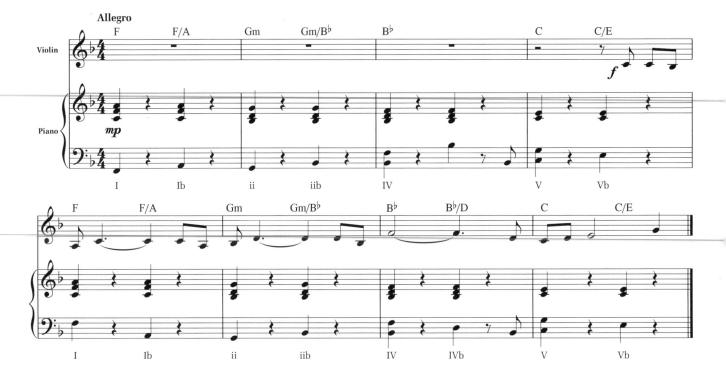

Broken chords

The notes of the chords are played one after another in an arpeggio pattern, which can be ascending, descending or both, as in the guitar picking in *House of the Rising Sun* performed The Animals. The right hand of the piano part in *Four Chord Brag* on page 66 uses broken chords.

A mixture of broken and block chords

This is commonly used in guitar strumming, such as in *What's Going On* by Marvin Gaye, and in the piano part in John Lennon's *Imagine*. Notice that in the next version of *Four Chord Brag* the bass line has extra notes added to make it more melodic.

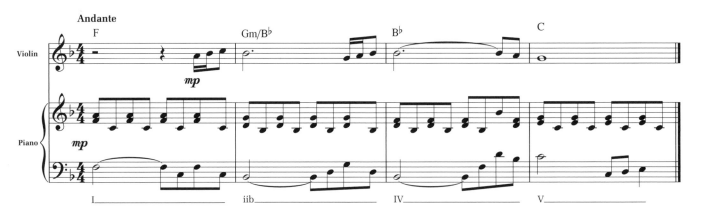

Bass notes and off-beat block chords

The accompaniment is split between bass notes on the strong beats of the bar, and block chords on the weaker beats. It is commonly used in waltzes like 'Aunt Marge's Waltz' from the soundtrack to *Harry Potter and the Prisoner of Azkaban* and marches like the 'Little People' theme from *Star Wars*.

Here is *Four Chord Brag* as a waltz:

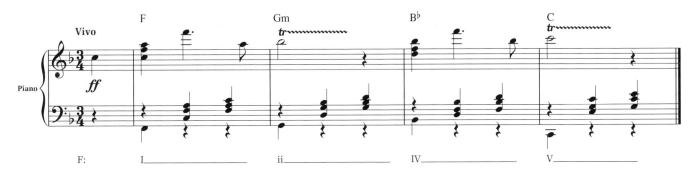

Here it is as a march. Notice that the bass part in bar 1 includes two passing notes to make it sound interesting.

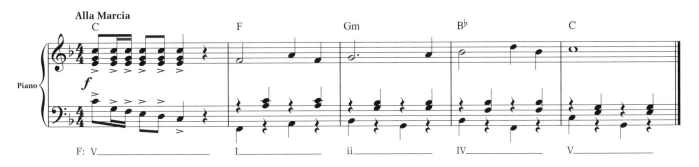

Keywords

Cadence, chord, chord symbols, interrupted cadence, imperfect cadence, major 3rd, major triad, minor 3rd, minor triad, passing note, perfect cadence, plagal cadence, Roman numerals, root.

Revision exercise

Answer these multiple choice questions:

1. Major and minor triads are both examples of:

   a) Notes

   b) Chords

   c) Cadences

   d) Accompaniments.

2. How are the notes in a chord written in a musical score?

   a) Vertically

   b) Like a scale

   c) Only in the treble clef

   d) Only in the bass clef.

3. How many different notes does a major or minor triad contain?

   a) One

   b) Two

   c) Three

   d) Four.

4. What is the best way to work out the notes of the G major triad?

   a) Play any three notes starting on G

   b) Play notes 1, 2, and 3 of a G major scale

   c) Play alternate notes going down from G

   d) Play notes 1, 3 and 5 of a G major scale.

5. What are the notes of a G minor triad?

   a) G B♭ D

   b) G B D

   c) G♭ B D

   d) G B D♭.

6. What are the terms given to the three notes in a triad, counting up from the bottom note?

   a) Bass, middle, top

   b) Root, 3rd, 5th

   c) One, two, three.

   d) Bass, tenor, soprano

7. A C major triad written in root position has which note as the lowest sounding note?

   a) C

   b) E

   c) E♭

   d) G.

8. An E minor triad written in first inversion has which note as the lowest sounding note?

   a) E

   b) G

   c) G♯

   d) B.

9. A B♭ major triad written in second inversion has which note as the lowest sounding note?

   a) B♭

   b) D

   c) D♭

   d) F.

10. Which of these sets of chord symbols is the correct way of labelling the following chords?

a) C – F/C – Am/C – G – C

b) C/C – F – Am – G/G – C

c) C – Am – F – G – C

d) C – Am/C – F/C – G – C.

11. Which of these sets of Roman numerals is the correct way of labelling the following chords?

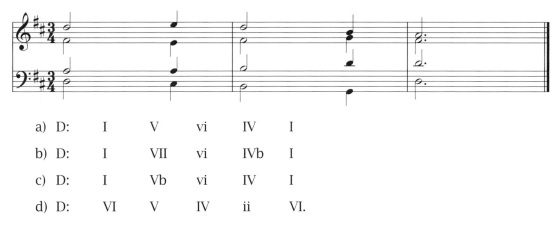

a) D: I   V   vi   IV   I

b) D: I   VII   vi   IVb   I

c) D: I   Vb   vi   IV   I

d) D: VI   V   IV   ii   VI.

12. What are the four types of cadence?

a) Major, minor, chord and triad

b) Sharp, flat, natural and accidental

c) Perfect, plagal, imperfect and interrupted

d) Tonic, root, 3rd and 5th.

13. Circle the non-harmony notes in the following piece of music. There are two in the flute part and two in the bass (left hand) of the piano part

Berkley: *Against the Clock*

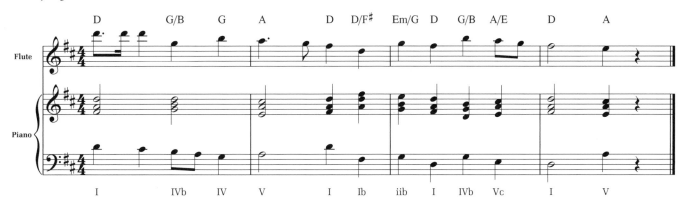

14. What type of non-harmony notes are used in question 13?

   a) They are wrong notes

   b) They are accidentals

   c) They are passing notes

   d) They are quavers.

15. What is the cadence at the end of this piece of music?

   a) Perfect

   b) Plagal

   c) Imperfect

   d) Interrupted.

7. Changing key: modulation and transposition

Modulation means changing key. A piece of music without modulation would be like eating a dinner consisting entirely of pasta! If we vary the keys used in a piece of music we have the ingredients for a gourmet meal.

Essential things you need to know about modulation

Modulation, or changing the key, gives a piece direction and variety.

Look at the short Christmas carol below and think about the following questions:

➢ What is the key signature?

➢ Does the key change at any point during the carol?

➢ How do you know?

➢ What might the new key be?

➢ Does the key change back again?

While Shepherds Watched (Tune by Handel)

While Shep - herds watched their flocks by night, all seat - ed on the ground, the

an - gel of the Lord came down and glo - ry shone a - round.

The key signature, together with the first chord, tells us that the piece starts in G major.

At the end of the first phrase ('seated on the ground') there is a modulation into D major.

There are two main features of modulation which help you to spot this:

➢ The C♯ accidentals. G major doesn't have C♯s, so their presence indicates that the key may have changed. D major does have both F♯ (like G major) and C♯, so it is likely that the new key is D major.

➢ The perfect cadence at the end of the modulated phrase in bars 3-4 is chords V–I of D major. This confirms that the new key is D major.

To modulate to a new key we need to identify which note(s) belong to the new key, but not the old – and introduce them into our piece.

> Remember:
> a tune in the
> key of G will
> use the notes
> of the G major
> scale in the
> melody and the
> accompaniment.

The following table shows the sharps of the keys involved in this particular modulation:

Original key	G Major	F#
New key	D Major	F# and C#

The new note in the new key (D major) is C#. This appears in bar 3.

The cadence in bars 3-4 is a perfect cadence using chords V and I of D major. By having the notes C# and D in the melody, we go from the leading note to the tonic of the new key – hence there's a very strong perfect cadence.

However, this modulation does not last long. A C major chord at the beginning of bar 5 immediately cancels the C#, returning us to a C natural. This removes us from D major and the return to G major (the tonic) is confirmed by a perfect cadence at the end of the carol.

Composers often use a **pivot chord** immediately before the cadence of a modulation to link together the different keys involved. This will be a chord that is common to both the old and the new key. In the carol above, we can see a B minor chord just before the D major perfect cadence (bar 3, second chord). So, how does B minor relate to the two keys? It is chord iii of G major (the old key) and chord vi of D major (the new key). Here, the B minor chord is a pivot chord.

Exercise 1

Which other minor chord could have been used as a pivot chord between G major and D major?

So, to spot and use modulations you need to know:

➢ Which notes belong to which key (revise scales if you are unsure of this)

➢ Which chords could act as pivot chords between the old and new keys

➢ How to spot and use cadences in different keys (revise harmony and cadences if you are unsure of this).

The carol above modulates from G major to D major and then back again. D is the fifth note of the G major scale. Fifth notes of scales are important for the harmony and are called the dominant notes. D major is therefore known as **the dominant** of G major.

Exercise 2

These two extracts modulate. Work out the original and new keys in each example, and name the accidental that is relevant to the modulation.

Haydn: Symphony No 94, '*Surprise*', 2nd movt.

Original key _____ New key _____ Accidental _____

Wade: *O Come All Ye Faithful*

Original key _____ New key _____ Accidental _____

Both of these examples modulate to the dominant (the most common modulation in music). The first one moves from C major to G major by adding an F♯.

The second example uses a B♮ as its modulating accidental. This is because we are moving from F major (which has a B♭) to C major (which does not have a B♭). Remember, accidentals in a modulation will not always be sharps - they may also be flats or naturals.

However, take care not to jump to conclusions about accidentals. They may not always be leading you to a modulation. They might be there simply to decorate the piece (as **chromatic notes**) or they could be part of a minor key, as in our next example.

Look at the following section from a waltz by Schubert, and think about these questions:

➢ Which key does Schubert start in?

➢ Which key does he end in at the start of bar 8?

➢ What is the relationship between the two keys?

Relative keys

Remember that relative keys share the same key signature but are based upon different scales. Look back at page 43 if you need to revise these.

Relative keys are always three semitones apart, going down from major to minor. For example, the relative of C major is A minor (C - B - B♭ - A = 3 semitones down).

The music clearly begins in A minor. We know this as there are no sharps or flats in the key signature, there are A minor triads in bars 1 and 3, and the use of a G♯ (from the harmonic minor scale) in bar 2. Therefore, the G♯ in this case does not indicate a modulation.

However, by bar 6, the G♯ has become a G♮ which suggests a move to the relative major. This is confirmed by a perfect cadence in C major (the relative major of A minor) between bars 7 and 8. Finally, notice the D♯ at the end of the extract. This is simply a chromatic note in the melody - it has no relevance to the modulation between A minor and C major.

How do you choose to which key to modulate?

Why change from G major to D major or from A minor to C major? Are these random choices? Many pieces follow this modulation pattern but is this a coincidence?

The answer is 'No': these keys are the closest keys harmonically to the tonic, or original key.

There is only one difference between the pitches of G major and D major - the latter uses C♯ rather than C♮ - and D is the important fifth note (dominant) of G major.

C major is the relative major of A minor (see Chapter 4: Scales if you need to revise this).

Modulations between the tonic key, dominant key and relative key are the most common in music.

We can show these key relationships with what is called the **circle of 5ths**. A section of it looks like this:

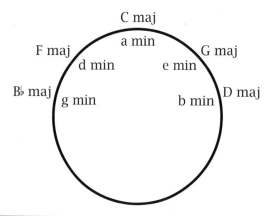

> ➤ The major keys run round the outside of the wheel

> ➤ The relative minors are on the inside

> ➤ It is called the circle of 5ths because each step clockwise round the circle is 5 notes of the scale apart (from C, if you count 5 notes of the C major scale you get G; from G, if you count 5 notes of the G major scale you get D, and so on).

To modulate to a new key, the easiest route to take is one step on the wheel in any direction. This could be clockwise, anticlockwise, inside or outside.

Look at G major. You could step anticlockwise to C major, clockwise to D major or step inside to E minor. To find out more about stepping anticlockwise, see opposite page.

This is exactly what our examples have done so far. You can now see that the choice of keys was not random, but followed this harmonic pattern.

The circle of keys continues round the circle in each direction.

Exercise 3
Complete the following table to revise what we have learnt so far.

Original key	Modulating to	New key	Accidentals required
G major	Dominant	D major	
D major		B minor	A♯
F major	Dominant		B♮
B♭ major	Relative minor		
C major	Relative minor		
C major			F♯
	Dominant	F major	
F major		D minor	
A minor			G♮

Extra things you might like to know about modulation

Modulating to the subdominant

Modulating to the dominant (clockwise round the circle of 5ths) is the most common direction to take, but composers may go anticlockwise instead.

Going down a 5th is the equivalent of going up a 4th, as can be seen by comparing the first and last boxes in the following diagram. If we start at C, then going down a 5th takes us to F. Going up a 4th also takes us to F.

F	G	A	B	C	D	E	F
5th down	4th down	3rd down	2nd down	starting point	2nd up	3rd up	4th up

This is why the fourth note of the scale is known as the subdominant: 'sub' means 'under' and 'dominant' is the name of the fifth degree of a scale. A modulation from C major to F major would be a modulation to the subdominant.

Look at the next example. Can you work out which keys the phrase starts and ends in?

Gilbert and Sullivan: from *Mikado*

The phrase starts in G major. However, the F♯ is 'cancelled' by an F♮ in the second bar. This gives us a perfect cadence in C major. C is the fourth note of the G major scale. Therefore, we have modulated to the subdominant.

More adventurous major and minor modulations

While modulations between the relative major and relative minor are very common in music ('hopping' inside and outside the circle of 5ths wheel above), you could also try some more adventurous major-minor changes. They can add some real colour and interest to your piece. Here is something a bit more dramatic by Haydn:

Haydn: Piano Sonata in C major, 1st movt.

> ➤ What key does it start in?

> ➤ Where is the modulation?

> ➤ How do you know?

> ➤ What is the new key?

The extract starts in C major (there are no sharps or flats in the key signature, there are C major chords and no accidentals).

The key changes in bar 8 – there are E♭ accidentals as part of an important broken chord in the left hand.

The new key is C minor, shown by the tonic triad of C minor (C – E♭ – G), emphasised through repetition in the left hand.

The key change is surprising. It is not to the dominant major (G major) or relative minor (A minor). Also, bar 7 uses the chords iib and V of C major, making us expect bar 8 to start with chord I of C major to make a perfect cadence to finish the phrase. Instead, we jump with no warning into a new phrase in C minor.

Therefore, switching between the tonic major and tonic minor does not necessarily require any special preparation, but can add some dramatic colour to your piece!

Modulations and musical structure

For a final example of modulation, we will look at a longer musical example and show how modulations can play an important role in helping to define the structure of a piece of music. Here is a Gavotte by J S Bach:

J S Bach: Gavotte

Allegretto

The piece has two main sections: bars 1-8, and bars 9-24. They are divided on the page by the double bar and the repeat marks, but they are divided musically as well.

The first modulation happens in the second half of section 1. The music moves from G major to D major. You can see this with the introduction of the C♯ in bar 5 and the perfect cadence between bars 7 and 8. The key change reinforces the piece's structure. It is a sort of musical journey: we set out and arrive in a new key. Later, we return home again.

There are further modulations in section 2. We will look for accidentals and a cadence to see if we can find them.

After the double bar, the C♯s have disappeared and so this tells us that we are now back in G major, which reinforces the fact that it is a new section of music. However, in bar 12 you will see C♯ and D♯, neither of which belong in G major. The new accidentals are a clue that we might be changing key again.

Which key, related to G major, might be suggested by the notes C♯ and D♯?

A likely candidate is E minor (see melodic minor scales in Chapter 4). E melodic minor uses the notes E F♯ G A B C♯ D♯ E in its ascending version and we can see the notes of this scale used in bars 12-16.

The second clue to a new key is the cadence of this phrase. The phrase ends in bars 15-16 with a perfect cadence in E minor. This confirms that we have changed key.

The final phrase of the Gavotte ends with a perfect cadence in G major, which shows that we have returned to the home key. The musical journey is complete!

So, to summarise modulation:

➢ If we want to move to the dominant key (clockwise round the wheel), we introduce the new note required by the dominant key

➢ If we want to move to the relative minor key (hopping inside the wheel), we introduce the raised 7th note from the harmonic minor scale; we could also introduce the raised 6th from the melodic minor scale

➢ To move to the relative major (hopping back outside the wheel), remove the sharpened 7th note from the harmonic minor scale (and the sharpened 6th if this was used)

➢ We reinforce our modulation with a perfect cadence in the new key

Although these are the most common modulations, there is no restriction as to what composers can do!

Transposition

Transposition means rewriting a passage of music at a different pitch while keeping the relationships (the number of tones or semitones) between the notes in the passage the same. It is seen commonly in music because some musical instruments are 'transposing instruments'. This means that the notes you see on the page are not the same as the ones you hear.

Look at the following arrangement of *Jingle Bells*, for the slightly unusual combination of trumpet and violin.

Pierpont: *Jingle Bells*

On first glance, it looks as though both the instruments are playing the same tune in completely different keys and we might well assume that it would sound absolutely terrible.

In fact, the instruments sound in **unison** (which means they play the same pitches at the same time). This is because we are using a trumpet in B flat, which is a **transposing instrument**.

When the player of an instrument 'in B♭' sounds the note C, it comes out as a B♭. Therefore, the part has to be written a tone above what you actually hear. The violin meanwhile is not a transposing instrument. Its part sounds the same as it looks: we can say that it plays at **concert pitch**.

It is therefore a useful skill to be able to transpose music, especially if you play a transposing instrument in an orchestra or band. Sometimes you may find that the part is in the 'wrong' key for your instrument. There are some other reasons why you might want to transpose passages of music:

➢ To copy an earlier passage of music into a new key when composing

➢ To move a vocal passage so that it can be sung within the range of a singer.

Let's suppose that we want to transpose the following simple tune up one tone:

Trad: *Twinkle Twinkle, Little Star*

We need to ask ourselves the following questions:

➢ What key is it in?

➢ What key will it be in if we move it one tone higher?

➢ What will our new key signature be – do we need sharps or flats?

Our tune is in C major and so by moving up one tone we will be in D major. We will need a key signature of two sharps (F♯ and C♯). All the notes will move up a tone: the C will move to a D, the G will move to an A, and so on. When we transpose a whole piece or passage, we would normally include the new key signature so that there are not lots of unnecessary accidentals. This is how the above tune would look if we transposed it up one tone:

A good music-notation programme will handle transposition in a few clicks and this can certainly save a lot of time and effort. However, it is still important to understand what the notation programme is actually doing, and the ability to transpose on an instrument or on paper is a very useful skill in itself.

You might also need to transpose music which contains some accidentals – this will frequently happen when the piece is in a minor key.

Exercise 4

We are going to transpose the following melody by Mozart up one tone.

Mozart: Symphony No 40, K550, 1st movt.

First we need to work out what key the piece is in. A two-flat key signature suggests either B♭ major or G minor. As there are some F♯s in the piece (which is the raised 7th note of the G minor scale), we might guess that this is in G minor.

If we are in G minor and transpose up one tone (two semitones), we move from G to A.

Therefore, the new key will be A minor, which does not have a key signature.

What will the starting note be? In the original we have an E♭. This will move up one tone to F♮.

Have a go at writing out the melody by Mozart on the lines below, up one tone to A minor.

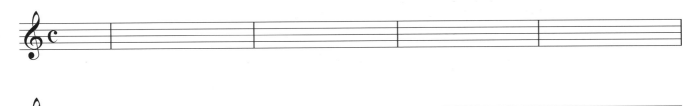

Exercise 5

Now, write out each of the following melodies, working out the required transposition. Use the key signature of the new key.

a) Transpose up one tone.

Bon Jovi: *Living on a Prayer*

b) Transpose down one tone.

Saint-Saëns: 'The Swan' from *Carnival of the Animals*

c) Transpose down one tone. Work out carefully what the new key signature will be. How will the C♯ in bar 3 be transposed down a tone? Write it in your transposed version.

Byrd: Galliard

d) Transpose up a minor 3rd (to A♭ major).

Vivaldi: 'Spring' from *The Four Seasons*

Exercise 6

a) Write out the following clarinet in B♭ part at concert pitch.

Hill: *Happy Birthday*

b) A friend wants to sing *Swing Low, Sweet Chariot*, but cannot sing the top notes. Rewrite the tune, down a 4th, so that it is in C major. Then try playing both versions.

Willis: *Swing Low, Sweet Chariot*

Shifting up a semitone in pop songs

Shifting up a semitone is an idea that occurs commonly in pop songs and links together modulation and transposition.

In a song, you might find that the last chorus shifts up a semitone, perhaps when the composer has run out of any better ideas! This is sometimes described as the 'truck driver's gear change' and has been used as a device to extend countless pop songs. It is a modulation, in the sense that the music changes key, but it is perhaps better to think of it as a transposition, in the sense that all the notes shift up a semitone.

A well-known pop song that includes this technique is Michael Jackson's *Man in the Mirror*, but perhaps one of the most exaggerated examples of this occurs in Stevie Wonder's *I Just Called to Say I Love You*. Not content with one semitone shift, he performs the trick twice in the song!

Keywords

Circle of 5ths, concert pitch, dominant, modulation, pivot chord, subdominant, tonic, transposing instruments, transposition, unison.

Revision exercise

Complete the blanks by selecting from the words, letters and symbols in the box below:

trumpet	C major	perfect	B♭	dominant	relative
modulation	accidentals	D major	transposition	C	

When you change key it is called a _____ You can spot one by looking out

for _____ of the new key and also a _____ cadence in the new key.

A very common modulation is to the key based upon the 5th note of the scale. This

is called the _____. It is also common to modulate from the major to its

_____ minor and vice versa.

It is easiest to modulate between keys that are closely related on the circle of 5ths.

Moving a series of notes into a new key is known as _____.

When the player of an instrument in B♭, such as a_____, plays the

note _____it comes out as a _____.

If you were in _____ and transposed your music up a tone, you would then

be in _____.

Answers

Chapter One

Exercise 1
2. 10
3. 12
4. 14
5. 7
6. 6

Exercise 2
2.
3.
4.
5.

Exercise 3
1. 4/4
2. 3/4
3. 2/4
4. 3/4

Exercise 4
1.
2.
3.
4.

Exercise 6
Row 2: 14

Row 3: 9

Row 4: 7

Row 5: 11

Row 6: 10

Exercise 7
1.
2.
3.
4.

Exercise 8

Exercise 9
2. A G F E D C B A
3. F G A B C D E F
4. G A B C D E F G
5. B A G F E D C B

Exercise 10
Violin: Treble
Soprano (voice): Treble
Descant recorder: Treble
Timpani: Bass
Oboe: Treble
Tuba: Bass
Bass (voice): Bass
Glockenspiel: Treble
Flute: Treble
Trumpet: Treble

Exercise 11

Twinkle, Twinkle Little Star

CCGG, AAG, FFEE, DDC

Minuet

GCDEF, GCC, AFGAB, CCC, FGFED, EFEDC, BCDEC, D

GCDEF, GCC, AFGAB, CCC, FGFED, EFEDC, DEDCB, C

Away in a Manger

G, CCDE, CCEF, GGA, FDE, FFG, EECE, DAC, BG

CCDE, CCEF, GGA, FDE, FFG, EECE, DAB, C

Over the Hills and Far Away

CDED, CDED, CA, AG, CDED, CDEC, FD, DG, CDED,
CDED, CAF, AGF, GE, FD, D

Revision exercise

We use **letter names** written as capital letters to
indicate pitch in music. We draw notes on a set of
five lines called a **stave**, and can place notes on the
lines and spaces. At the start of each stave we draw
a **clef**. For higher pitched music we use a **treble clef**,
and for lower pitched music we use a **bass clef**. If we
need to write notes that go above or below the stave,
we use **leger lines**.

Chapter Two

Exercise 1

1.

2.

3.

Exercise 2

1.

2.

3.

Exercise 3

Exercise 4

Row 2: higher, F

Row 3: higher, C

Row 4: lower, B

Exercise 5

1. C, FFGAGG, FDCC, FEFG, AB♭AG

2. A, DDEDC♯, BBB, EEF♯ED, C♯AA, F♯F♯GF♯E, DBAA, BEC♯, D

3. DFA, DEFGFEDC♯, ADFAFDB♭, GCEGECA

4. DEDC♯, C♮E, DG, G, GAGF♯, GE, D, D

Revision exercise

Key signature: A collection of sharps or flats written
at the start of every stave

Natural: A sign cancelling the effect of a previous
sharp of flat written as anaccidental or in the key
signature

Sharp: A sign that indicates that a note is a semitone
higher than its normal unaltered pitch

Flat: A sign which indicates that a note is a semitone
lower than its normal unaltered pitch

Chapter Three

Exercise 1

Exercise 2

2.

3.

Exercise 3

1. $\frac{5}{4}$

2. $\frac{9}{4}$

3. $\frac{7}{4}$

Exercise 4

1. Bar 4 - $\frac{2}{4}$, bar 5 - $\frac{4}{4}$, bar 6 - $\frac{5}{4}$

2. Bar 3 - $\frac{6}{8}$, bar 4 - $\frac{3}{4}$, bar 5 - $\frac{2}{4}$, bar 7 - $\frac{3}{4}$

3. Bar 3 - $\frac{7}{4}$, bar 4 - $\frac{5}{4}$, bar 5 - $\frac{6}{8}$, bar 6 - $\frac{4}{4}$

Exercise 5

The time signature alternates between $\frac{5}{4}$ and $\frac{6}{4}$ for each bar.

Revision exercise

a) The **pulse** is what you tap your foot to. The **tempo** is how fast you tap your foot. Tempo markings are often given in Italian, though you will find them in other languages too.

b) Table 1 (in order):
Moderato, Adagio, Largo, Prestissimo, Allegro, Presto, Andante, Vivace.

c) Table 2 (in order):
Più mosso, Meno mosso, Ritardando, A tempo, Accelerando.

d) A time signature of $\frac{2}{2}$ shows that the beat should be counted in **minims**.

If you want a piece with a beat of three minims per bar, then you should use a time signature of $\frac{3}{2}$.

A cut-C time signature can be used instead of $\frac{2}{2}$.

A Jig will often have a time signature of $\frac{6}{8}$. This is known as a **compound** time signature, where the beat is a **dotted crotchet**.

Chapter Four

Exercise 1

C major: CDEFGABC

G major: GABCDEF♯G

F major: FGAB♭CDEF

B♭ major: B♭CDE♭FGAB♭

A major: ABC♯DEF♯G♯A

E♭ major: E♭FGA♭B♭CDE♭

Exercise 2

D major

A major

B♭ major
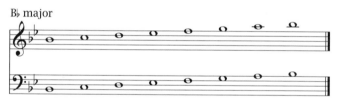

E♭ major
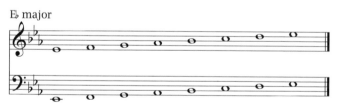

Exercise 3

A harmonic minor, relative minor of C major
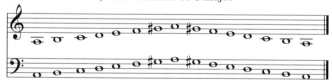

B harmonic minor, relative minor of D major
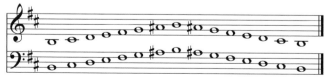

F# harmonic minor, relative minor of A major

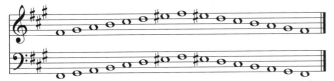

D harmonic minor, relative minor of F major

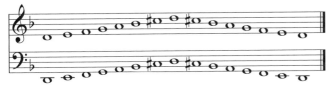

G harmonic minor, relative minor of B♭ major

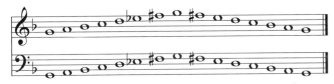

C harmonic minor, relative minor of E♭ major

Exercise 4

B melodic minor

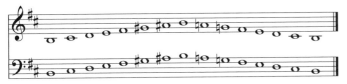

F# melodic minor

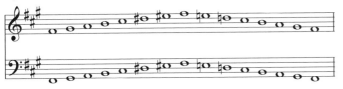

D melodic minor

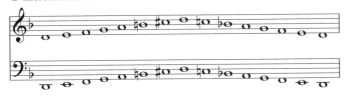

G melodic minor

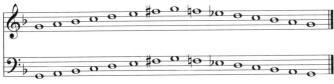

C melodic minor

Revision exercise

Row 1: C major

Row 2: E minor, G minor

Row 3: F# and C#

Row 4: F#, C# and G#

Row 5: D minor

Row 6: G minor, B♭ and E♭

Row 7: E♭ major

Multiple choice questions

1. Tones and semitones.

2. The smallest possible interval between two adjacent notes on a keyboard.

3. An interval of two semitones.

4. T - T - ST - T - T - T - ST.

5. The first note of a major scale and of a minor scale.

6. F#.

7. They share the same key signature.

8. Harmonic and melodic.

9. A semitone.

10. You raise notes 6 and 7 by a semitone in the ascending form of the scale and lower notes 6 and 7 back again by a semitone in the descending form of the scale.

Chapter Five

Exercise 1

Exercise 2

Exercise 3

Below is one suggested answer. (Alternatively phrase marks may be placed over bars 1-8 and 9-16.)

Exercise 4

One, two, buckle my shoe
Three, four, shut the door
Five, six, pick up sticks
Seven, eight, lay them straight.

There was a Young Lady whose eyes,
Were unique as to colour and size;
When she opened them wide,
People all turned aside,
And started away in surprise.

Exercise 6

Exercise 7

Letter	What it is / is short for	What it tells you to do
B	slur	Join these notes together without separating them
C	crescendo	Get louder gradually
D	staccato	These notes should be short and separate from each other
E	fortissimo	Very loudly
F	diminuendo	Get softer gradually
G	accent	Play the note more loudly, or emphasise it more
H	piano	Play softly

Chapter Six

Exercise 1

b) F♯ minor

c) F major

d) C minor

Exercise 2

C major, E minor, B minor, A major

Exercise 3

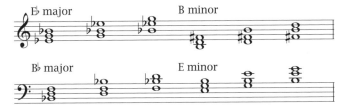

Exercise 4

G major, A minor, D minor, C major, B minor, F major, E minor and B♭ major

Exercise 5

A major, G minor, B♭ major, C minor, E♭ major and A minor

Exercise 6

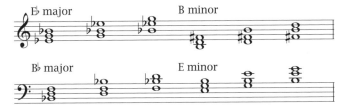

Exercise 7

D major, first inversion

C♯ major, second inversion

F♯ major, root position

A♭ major, second inversion

F minor, first inversion

G minor, second inversion

C minor, root position

D minor, first inversion

Revision exercise

1. Chords.

2. Vertically.

3. Three.

4. Play notes 1, 3 and 5 of a G major scale.

5. G B♭ D.

6. Root, 3rd, 5th.

7. C.

8. G.

9. F.

10. C–Am/C–F/C–G–C.

11. D: I   Vb   vi   IV   I.

12. Perfect, plagal, imperfect and interrupted.

13. The crotchet C♯, piano LH bar 1; the quaver A, piano LH bar 1; the quaver G, flute bar 2; the quaver G, flute bar 3.

14. They are passing notes.

15. Imperfect.

Chapter Seven

Exercise 1

E minor.

Exercise 2

1. Original key: C major

    New key: G major

    Accidental: F sharp.

2. Original key: F major

    New key: C major

    Accidental: B natural.

Exercise 3

Row 1: C#

Row 2: Relative minor

Row 3: C major

Row 4: G minor, F#

Row 5: A minor, G#

Row 6: Dominant, G major

Row 7: B♭ major, E♮

Row 8: Relative minor, C#

Row 9: Relative major, C major

Exercise 4

Exercise 5

a)

b)

c)

d)

Exercise 6

a)

b)

Revision exercise

When you change key it is called a **modulation**. You can spot modulations by looking out for **accidentals** of the new key and also a **perfect** cadence in the new key.

A very common modulation is to the key based upon the fifth note of the scale. This is called the **dominant**. It is also common to modulate from the major to its **relative** minor and vice versa.

It is easiest to modulate between keys that are closely related on the circle of 5ths.

When you move a series of notes up or down in pitch, it is known as **transposition**. When the player of an instrument in B♭, such as the **trumpet**, plays the note **B♭** it comes out as a **C**.

If you were in **C major** and transposed your music up a tone, you would then be in **D major**.